BIG BANG, SMALL VOICE

BIG BANG, SMALL VOICE

Reconciling Genesis and Modern Science

2nd edition

P.G.Nelson

Botanic Christian Books

Published by
Botanic Christian Books
25–27 Duesbery Street,
Hull, HU5 3QE

© P.G.Nelson 2014
1st edition P.G.Nelson 1999
Reprinted with corrections 2003

ISBN 978-0-9928256-0-7

Printed by Charlesworth Press, Wakefield

Contents

Acknowledgements

In writing this book I am indebted to a great many people: to friends who have been praying for me while I have been doing it; to colleagues with whom I have discussed the question of origins, in some cases over many years; to the many authors whose writings have influenced my thinking; and to those who have skilfully converted my manuscript and sketches into a book.

I am particularly grateful to the late Dr. John Bradley, Professor Nigel Cutland, the late Rev. Ronald Evans, the Rev. Dr. Arthur Fraser, and Dr. Geoff. Oldershaw, for discussions going back 30 years; to anti-evolutionist Malcolm Bowden, the late Professor Donald Mackay, Prebendary Dr. Victor Pearce, and the Rev. Sir John Polkinghorne, F.R.S., for helpful correspondence on their own thinking; to Dr. Oliver Barclay for kindly reading through and commenting on the text; to Meg and Brian Deakin for typing it; and Dr. Keith Whittles for publishing it. As always I remain responsible for the views expressed and for any errors, for which I apologise.

Second edition

I am grateful to all those who have continued to encourage me. These include Dr. Oliver Barclay and Dr. Geoff Oldershaw, both of whom have sadly now died. Dr. Barclay kindly wrote that *Big Bang, Small Voice* "is a distinctive Bible-believing contribution to the discussions, and will I trust be taken seriously by all involved in the debates."

In memory of Dr. John Bradley and the Reverend Ronald Evans, two godly and careful scholars, one a scientist with interests in theology, the other a theologian with interests in science: mentors both.

...and after the fire
a still small voice

(1 Kings 19: 11–12)

Part I

Introduction and Background

1 Introduction

This book is concerned with the tension between the Biblical account of the origin of the universe and that given by modern science. According to the Bible, God created the universe in six days a few thousand years ago. According to modern science, however, the universe started in a Big Bang about 10–15 billion (thousand million) years ago, and gradually evolved into its present state.

The tension between these two accounts is widely felt. It poses a problem to many non-Christians in considering the claims of Christianity, and to many Christians in thinking about their faith.[1] It poses a particular problem to those Christians who believe that the Bible has been inspired by God, and is authoritative in its teaching. Some theologians argue that the Biblical account should not be taken literally,[2] but to others, not taking it literally greatly weakens the Bible's authority.[3] Many Christians find it difficult to accept that God created nature, in Tennyson's words, "red in tooth and claw".[4]

In this book I shall seek to resolve the problem in the following way. I shall first assume that the scientific account is correct, and examine how far the Biblical account can be reconciled to it without weakening the Bible's authority (Part II). I shall then assume that the Biblical account, taken literally, is correct, and examine how far the scientific account can be reconciled to this without distorting science (Part III). Finally, I shall

---

[1] Cf. Rendle-Short, *Green Eye of the Storm* (a biography of four Christian scientists troubled by evolution).
[2] E.g., Blocher, *In the Beginning*; Ward, *God, Chance and Necessity*, pp. 62–63.
[3] E.g., Young, *In the Beginning*; Cameron, *Evolution and the Authority of the Bible*.
[4] Tennyson, *In Memoriam* 56.

bring the results of the two investigations together, and draw some conclusions (Part IV).

To make the discussion accessible to as many readers as possible, I shall keep the use of technical language to a minimum. I shall also refer mainly to books written at an introductory or popular level. In Chapter 2 I briefly describe the scientific account of origins, in Chapters 3 and 4 the Biblical account, and in Chapter 5 evidence for the flood described in the Bible. Readers who are already familiar with this material can omit these chapters if they wish.

Quotations from the Bible are based on the New King James Version and the New International Version. In dates B.P. means "before present".

Update

This edition includes an update at the end (pages 141–157), divided into the same sections as the text. These are best read after the corresponding section in the text. There is also a supplement to the Bibliography (pages 170–174). This is selective, there having been a great many publications in the field since the first edition.

2 Scientific account of origins

Most scientists currently believe that the universe started as a speck of highly concentrated matter, which rapidly expanded, and gradually developed into the universe as we now know it.[1] As far as the earth is concerned, this development took place in four phases. The first was the evolution of the cosmos, and the formation of the solar system ("cosmic evolution"). The second was the cooling down of the earth and development of its crust ("geological evolution"). The third phase was the formation of increasingly complicated chemicals in lakes and seas, and the generation from these of the first living organisms ("chemical evolution"). The final phase was the evolution of more complex organisms, leading to the plants and animals on the earth today ("biological evolution").

In the following sections I shall briefly discuss the evidence for these stages of evolution. I shall also discuss alternative theories that have been proposed, both within orthodox science, and, in Section 2.6, by Biblical Christian scientists who believe that orthodox science is wrong.

2.1 Big bang and cosmic evolution

The idea that the universe began in a big bang is based on the study of galaxies.[2] These are large clusters of stars, like the Milky Way, to which the Sun belongs. Distant galaxies look like single stars to the naked eye, and very distant ones can only been seen through a telescope.

A feature of distant galaxies is that the light coming from them is

---

[1] See, e.g., Weinberg and others, "Life in the Universe"; Delsemme, *Our Cosmic Origins*.
[2] See, e.g., Weinberg, *The First Three Minutes*; Silk, *The Big Bang*; Barrow and Silk, *The Left Hand of Creation*; Silk, *A Short History of the Universe*.

redder than that from similar sources closer to the earth. (More technically, if the light is split up into its components, the colour of each component is shifted towards the red end of the spectrum.) Astronomers interpret this reddening as indicating that distant galaxies are moving away from the earth, and that the universe is expanding.

Cosmologists infer from this expansion that the universe once had a small volume and started in an explosion. By using accepted theories of physics to describe the later stages of the process, and developing new ones to describe the early stages, they have sought to work out the details of the explosion, and to explain the present structure of the universe.

In this they have had considerable success. They have been able to explain the proportion of the two lightest gases in the universe (hydrogen and helium), as estimated from astronomical observations. They predicted the existence of a weak background radiation in space, which was subsequently discovered. They also predicted small variations in the average energy of this radiation, for which some evidence has been obtained.

At the time of writing, however, cosmologists have difficulty in explaining all the features of the universe on a big-bang model. In particular:

(1) The distribution of galaxies is not as uniform as the model predicts. The distribution is like a huge sponge, with large holes in it.

(2) On the standard model, cosmologists calculate that there is ten times more matter in the universe than astronomers can observe directly. Astronomers have evidence that there is additional matter in the universe (called "dark matter") from its gravitational effect on visible bodies, but not in the amounts required by the model.

These discrepancies can be removed by introducing a "cosmological constant" (an extra factor) into the equations, but there is as yet no independent evidence for this factor.[3]

Most cosmologists are cautiously optimistic that further work will

---

[3] Coles, "The End of the Old Model Universe".

overcome these problems. However, some reject the big bang, and prefer other models, which I discuss below.[4]

Note that the observations that lead astronomers to conclude that the universe is expanding establish an absolute time scale for the universe.[5] At first sight, this appears to conflict with Einstein's theory of relativity. On this theory, events that appear to take place at the same time to one observer can appear to take place at different times to another observer if he or she is moving at speed relative to the first. However, this only means that an absolute time scale cannot be derived from arbitrary observations of this kind (i.e. from observations of events that bear no obvious temporal relationship to each other). It does not mean that there is no absolute scale.

Other models

Several alternatives to the big bang have been suggested.[6] These are of three kinds:

(1) *Models on which the universe has always been in existence.* These include the following:

- STATIC MODELS On these the universe does not change in size, and the reddening of light from distant galaxies is attributed to another cause (e.g. tiring of light as it travels through space, or shrinkage of atoms over time).

- STEADY-STATE MODEL On this the universe expands from a point in the infinite past, and matter is continuously created within it. This model does not account for the weak background radiation, for which some other explanation has to be found.

- CYCLICAL MODEL On this the universe goes through a continuous cycle of expansion and contraction (big bang, expansion, contraction, big crunch, big bang, expansion, contraction, big crunch, etc.).

---

[4] E.g., Lerner, *The Big Bang Never Happened.*
[5] Narlikar, *The Primeval Universe*, pp. 53–56.
[6] Silk, *The Big Bang*, Chap. 18.

• MATTER-ANTIMATTER MODEL This is based on the properties of plasmas (electrified gases) and on the assumption that the universe contains equal quantities of matter and antimatter (the electrical opposite of ordinary matter). On this model the universe contracts until it reaches a certain size, then expands.

(2) *Model on which the concept of a beginning has no meaning.* On the big-bang model, the universe starts off microscopically small. Stephen Hawking applied the theory of microscopic systems (the quantum theory) to the universe, and produced a model on which time and distance are indistinguishable.[7] There is accordingly no identifiable beginning to the universe, because there is no identifiable beginning of time. However, the indistinguishability only applies while the universe is very small.[8] When it gets larger, a time scale can be established from the expansion. The idea of a beginning can accordingly be recovered by extrapolating the latter scale back into the microscopic stage.

(3) *Models involving more than one universe.* These include the idea that there are an infinite number of universes, and the suggestion that a universe can divide or generate other universes.[9] I shall discuss these ideas further in a later chapter.

2.2 Geological evolution

Most geologists believe that the earth has developed into its present form over a long period of time. This belief is based on several lines of evidence, including the following.[10]

Structure of crust

In many places, the upper part of the earth's crust consists of many distinct layers of rock (strata) one on top of the other. Examination of these layers shows that most of them have been formed by the accumulation

---

[7] Hawking, *A Brief History of Time.*
[8] Davies, *The Mind of God*, pp. 61–68.
[9] See, e.g., Leslie, *Universes.*
[10] See, e.g., Press and Siever, *Earth*; *Understanding Earth.*

and consolidation of sediment — either fragments of pre-existing rock (e.g. sandstone), or material deposited from water (e.g. rock salt), or the remains of animals or plants (e.g. coal). Some rock formations comprise many thousands of different strata, and are thousands of metres thick.

Beds of sediment are being laid today. Some are being laid gradually, at a low rate (e.g. on the ocean floor). Others are being laid in an episodic manner, with short periods of rapid deposition, followed by long periods of erosion (e.g. on flood plains). In either case the average rate of deposition is low. If beds in the past were laid at this kind of rate, the time taken for a series of strata to have formed will have been considerable.

At one time geologists thought that all the processes involved in crustal evolution were of a kind that can be observed today ("uniform-itarianism"). They now believe that many strata were laid under more dramatic conditions, as could arise, for example, if a large meteorite struck the earth or a large volcano erupted. This explains the formation of large fossils, e.g. of dinosaurs or upright trees. According to Derek Ager, a leading exponent of this view, "the history of any one part of the earth, like the life of a soldier, consists of long periods of boredom and short periods of terror".[11] Note that geologists still envisage these catastrophic events as conforming to the laws of physics and chemistry, and as being "uniform" in this sense.[12]

Fossils

Many sedimentary rocks contain fossils. Fossils are formed when dead organisms sink into mud that subsequently dries out and hardens, or when living organisms are suddenly overwhelmed by muddy flood-water that leaves them engulfed in mud.

The fossils in a rock generally differ from one layer or set of layers to another. This suggests that the organisms that populated a region when one set was laid were different from those when the next set was laid.

---

[11] Ager, *The Nature of the Stratigraphical Record*, p. 141; *The New Catastrophism*, pp. xix, 197–198.
[12] Press and Siever, *Earth*, pp. 37–38; *Understanding Earth*, pp. 164–165.

Further, fossil-bearing strata almost invariably occur in the same order according to the kinds of fossil they contain (e.g. those containing both jawless fish and jawed fish above those containing only jawless fish). The exceptions are generally in locations where there is evidence of a major disturbance of land mass. This pattern suggests a history of the earth marked by distinct phases (e.g. a phase when all fish were jawless).

This history is shown in Table 2.1. Features of this history are:

- the appearance of new species, including major new types (column 2);
- a proliferation of new types in the Cambrian period (the "Cambrian explosion");
- the continuance of some species, and the disappearance of others, sometimes in large numbers ("mass extinctions").

Table 2.1   Phases in the history of the earth inferred from fossils.[a]

Phase[b]	Major new types of organism
Precambrian	bacteria, algae
Late Precambrian	water-worms, sponges
Cambrian	various kinds of shellfish
Ordovician	fish
Silurian	land plants
Devonian	insects, amphibians
Carboniferous	reptiles
Permian	large reptiles
Triassic	
Jurassic	mammals, birds
Cretaceous	flowering plants
Tertiary	primates
Quaternary	humans

[a] Press and Siever, *Understanding Earth*; Weinberg and others, "Life in the Universe"; Kerr, "Pushing Back the Origins of Animals".

[b] Geologists call all except the Precambrian *periods*. They group periods into *eras* and divide them into *epochs*.

Geologists attribute mass extinctions to catastrophes, or other environmental changes.

Radiometric dating

Geologists date rocks by radiometric methods.[13] These are based on the observation that certain kinds of atom break down by radioactive decay into other kinds (e.g. uranium-235 into lead-207), and generally do so at a constant rate (i.e. a constant percentage of atoms per second). By measuring this rate and the number of "parent" and "daughter" atoms in a mineral from a rock, the age of the rock can be calculated, provided that:

(1) the mineral was formed at the same time as the rock it is in;

(2) there has been no loss or gain of parent or daughter atoms since the mineral was formed, other than by radioactive decay of the parent;

(3) the number of daughter atoms in the mineral at the time of its formation can be estimated in some way;

(4) the rate of decay has remained constant over the life-time of the rock.

Rocks that are most likely to satisfy conditions (1)–(3) are undisturbed igneous rocks (rocks that have been formed by solidification of the molten material now lying underneath the earth's crust, e.g. granites). For these (1) and (2) can be expected to hold, and (3) can be achieved fairly easily.[14] When different radiometric methods are applied to such rocks, the results for some agree to better than ±5% (for others disturbance is suspected).[15]

Radiometric dating cannot generally be applied to sedimentary rocks. For these geologists rely partly on relative dates, estimated by comparing

---

[13] Eicher, *Geologic Time*.

[14] For example, lead-207 atoms in minerals are accompanied by lead-204 atoms, which, as far as is known, are not formed or lost by radioactive decay. One can therefore use the ratio of lead-207 to lead-204 atoms in a uranium-free mineral in a rock (generally about 16:1) to estimate the original number of lead-207 atoms in a uranium-containing mineral in the rock (= about 16 times the number of lead-204 atoms).

[15] York and Farquhar, *The Earth's Age and Geochronology*, p. 75.

Table 2.2 Chronology of earth history.[a]

Event	Date (millions of years B.P.)
Formation of earth	4,500
First rocks	4,000
First microfossils	3,500
Cambrian	570
Ordovician	510
Silurian	440
Devonian	410
Carboniferous	360
Permian	290
Triassic	250
Jurassic	210
Cretaceous	140
Tertiary	65
Quaternary	2
	0

[a] Press and Siever, *Understanding Earth*; Weinberg and others, "Life in the Universe" (rounded).

sequences of strata and assuming that the rates of sedimentation, or of changes in fossils, are the same. Absolute dates can be obtained if, for example, between two strata there is a layer of solidified lava from a nearby volcano. The age of this igneous material sets a lower limit to the age of strata below it and an upper limit to the age of strata above it. From such data, approximate dates have been assigned to the different geological periods, as shown in Table 2.2.

A science writer has pointed out that the time intervals in this table correspond to very low rates of sedimentation, calculated from the total thickness of strata formed in each period.[16] These average 0.2 millimetre

[16] Milton, *The Facts of Life*, Fig. 1 (facing p. 144).

per year. To explain this figure it is necessary to suppose that lasting deposits are formed either very slowly or at very infrequent intervals (e.g. deposits 20 centimetres thick once every 1,000 years).

A feature of the chronology in Table 2.2 is the relatively long period between the appearance of the first fossils and the Cambrian (about 3,000 million years, compared with 500 million from the first rocks to the first fossils, and 500 million from the Cambrian to the present).

Alternative geologies

Some Biblical Christian scientists have put forward an alternative geology to the above. I discuss this in Section 2.6.

2.3 Chemical evolution: the origin of life

Most chemists working on the origin of life assume that this took place in the waters of the primitive earth, in the interval between the formation of the first lakes and seas and the appearance of the first fossils, about 3,800–3,500 million years ago (cf. Table 2.2). They further assume that the first organisms were formed from simple chemicals containing the same groups of atoms as the chemicals that make up living organisms. In the simple chemicals (e.g. amino-acids) the groups exist separately, but in organisms they are joined together. For example, proteins comprise groups of atoms of 20 different kinds joined together in long and cross-linked chains, as illustrated in Figure 2.1. Chemists know that the separate groups will join together under suitable conditions. They are therefore working on (1) how the simple chemicals containing these groups could have been formed, and (2) how the groups joined together in the primitive waters to produce the first living organisms.

The first task is easier than the second. Chemists have proposed several ways in which the basic chemicals could have been produced:

- by the action of lightning on the primitive atmosphere (assumed to be low in oxygen);
- by processes taking place in space, the chemicals being carried to earth on meteorites or cosmic dust;

```
GIVEQC —— CSLYQLENYCN
   CTSI                    |
    |                      |
FVNQHLCGSHLVEALYLVCGERGFFYTPKT
```

Figure 2.1   A small protein molecule (human insulin). Different groups of atoms are indicated by letters. C groups cross-link. Under ordinary conditions the chains are wrapped round each other. A sample of insulin comprises a large number of such units, weakly held together. Insulin from other animals is similar, but not identical (e.g. bovine insulin has CASV instead of CTSI in the first chain and PKA instead of PKT in the second). (From Croft, *Handbook of Protein Sequences*.)

> • by processes taking place around underwater cracks in the earth's crust.

The second task is very difficult. Even the simplest organisms are extremely complicated chemical systems, comprising a great many chemicals, each with its own particular sequence of groups. Chemists accordingly face formidable difficulties in trying to work out how the first organisms arose. All they can do at the present time is to sketch in very general terms possible ways in which life could have arisen.

Most chemists who are working on the problem acknowledge that the origin of life is still very much a mystery.[17] Stuart Kauffman states bluntly:[18]

> Anyone who tells you that he or she knows how life started... is a fool or a knave. Nobody knows.

---

[17] Cf. Shapiro, *Origins: A Skeptic's Guide to the Creation of Life on Earth*; Scott, *The Creation of Life: Past, Future, Alien*; Lynch, *Life is Impossible*; Maddox, "Frontiers of Ignorance".
[18] Kauffman, *At Home in the Universe* (p. 31, Viking edn.).

Other theories

Some scientists have attempted to calculate the chances that life evolved on earth, knowing the kinds of chemicals that have to be produced. They equate the chances of forming a particular protein to 1/20 (the chance that the first group of atoms is right, out of the 20 different kinds in proteins) times 1/20 (the chance that the second group is right) times 1/20 for the third group, and so on. For a protein of any size, the chances calculated in this way are extremely small, especially in relation to the time available for life to evolve on earth (about 300 million years on the above figures). This has prompted some scientists to suggest that life originated in space, and then came to earth.[19]

These calculations take no account of the natural tendency for chemicals to combine in particular ways, especially when they are in the presence of other chemicals, and form part of a complex system.[20] Even so, it is difficult to see how the odds of life evolving on earth can be very high when key chemicals in organisms are composed of groups of atoms that can be joined together in many different sequences.

Scientists are looking for life elsewhere in the universe. At the time of writing, some claim they have evidence of life on Mars, but this is controverted.

2.4   Biological evolution

Most biologists believe that plants and animals have evolved from simpler forms of life (Fig. 2.2), by a mechanism involving mutations and natural selection.[21] The theory combines Darwin's ideas in *The Origin of Species* with a modern understanding of genetics.

A mutation is an inheritable change in an organism's genes (the chemicals that determine an organism's characteristics). Mutants that

---

[19] Hoyle and Wickramasinghe, *Evolution from Space* and other writings; Crick, *Life Itself.*
[20] Kenyon and Steinman, *Biochemical Predestination*; Jantsch, *The Self-organizing Universe*; Kauffman, *The Origins of Order*; *At Home in the Universe*; de Duve, *Vital Dust.*
[21] See, e.g., Ridley, *Evolution.*

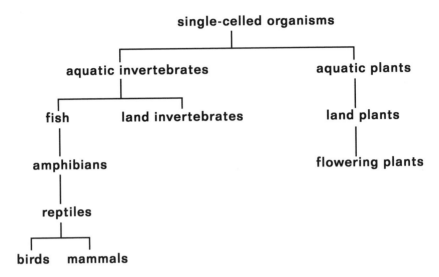

Figure 2.2 Order of evolution of major types of organisms. New types evolve from early forms of old types.

are better equipped to survive and reproduce in a particular environment than unchanged members of a species gradually replace the latter in this environment. Likewise species that are better able to cope with a change in an environment replace those that are not. This is natural selection. The theory is that evolution takes place gradually, in steps. Species A produces a successful mutant A′, which produces successful mutant A″, and so on, leading eventually to a new type of organism, B.

That small changes in organisms can take place by mutation and natural selection is well established. For example, geneticists have produced new strains of bacteria by placing an old strain in a harsh chemical environment and subjecting it to X-rays to produce mutations. Under these conditions, a strain that can cope better with the harsh environment takes over from the original one.[22] (This is not the same as adaptation, using existing genes.)

---

[22] Strickberger, *Genetics*, pp. 765–766.

However, large-scale evolutionary changes, as from a reptile to a bird or a mammal ("macroevolution"), are more controversial. While most biologists regard the evidence for such changes to be good, some do not. This division cuts across religious convictions. Many Biblical Christian biologists are in the first group, e.g. Douglas Spanner (*Biblical Creation and the Theory of Evolution*) and "Sam" Berry (*God and Evolution* and *God and the Biologist*). On the other hand, some secular biologists have been strongly critical of the evidence, e.g. G.A. Kerkut (*Implications of Evolution*) and Michael Denton (*Evolution: A Theory in Crisis*). Denton now finds big changes more plausible genetically, but not their random origin (*Nature's Destiny*).

A strong supporter of the theory is zoologist Richard Dawkins, author of *The Selfish Gene* and other books (see Bibliography). Strong opponents include Biblical Christian biologists Lane Lester and Raymond Bohlin (*The Natural Limits to Biological Change*), biochemist Duane Gish (*Evolution: The Fossils Say No!* and *Evolution: The Challenge of the Fossil Record*), engineer Luther Sunderland (*Darwin's Enigma*), and lawyer Phillip Johnson (*Darwin on Trial* and other books).

The main lines of evidence for macroevolution, and the difficulties associated with them, are as follows.[23]

Small changes

The fact that small evolutionary changes can take place supports the idea that large changes can occur by a succession of small ones over a period of time. However, since only small changes have been observed, the evidence could indicate that there are limits to the amount of genetic variation an organism can sustain, and that evolution can only take place within these limits.[24]

Fossil sequences

As discussed in Section 2.2, in rocks containing a series of fossil-bearing strata, there is generally a progression in the fossils in going up the series.

[23] Cf. Ridley, *Evolution*, Chap. 3; *The Problems of Evolution*.
[24] Cf. Denton, *Evolution: A Theory in Crisis*, Chap. 4.

The lowest strata contain only fossils having a relatively simple anatomy, and species of increasing complexity appear as the series is ascended. Where exceptions to this pattern occur, there are usually signs that the rock has been disturbed since the strata were laid. The order in which major new types of organism appear (Table 2.1) is the same as that proposed by biologists (Fig. 2.2).

The main problem with this evidence is that there are gaps in the fossil sequences. If evolution took place in steps, there ought to be series of gradually changing fossils linking different types of organism (e.g. between reptiles and birds or mammals). This was certainly Darwin's expectation in *The Origin of Species*. However, while there are some fossils that could be transitional (e.g. fossils of small animals from the Triassic period having both a reptilian and a mammalian jaw joint[25]), their number is small compared with the total number of fossils, and they could be variants or mutants of nontransitional species.[26]

Evolutionary biologists get over this difficulty, partly by insisting that some fossils are of transitional forms,[27] and partly by arguing that major stages of evolution could have taken place relatively quickly, in isolated populations.[28] Under these circumstances, the transitional forms would not have been present in sufficient numbers, or for long enough periods of time, for many fossils, if any, to form. Another suggestion, put forward by Michael Denton in his recent book[29], is that gradual genetic changes could sometimes accumulate without affecting an organism, and then abruptly produce a major change. I discuss this below.

Similarities between organisms

All except the simplest organisms (viruses and viroids) have the same basic constitution. They are all made up of cells, and in the cells they all

---

[25] Crompton and Jenkins, "Origin of Mammals"; Kemp, *Mammal-like Reptiles and the Origin of Mammals*.

[26] Cf. Denton, *Evolution: A Theory in Crisis*, Chaps. 8–9.

[27] Berry, *God and Evolution*, pp. 116–118.

[28] Eldredge and Gould, "Punctuated Equilibria: An Alternative to Phyletic Gradualism"; Berry, *God and Evolution*, p. 118.

[29] Denton, *Nature's Destiny*, pp. 278–279.

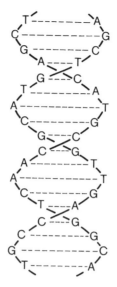

Figure 2.3 Constitution of a DNA molecule, the chemical that determinines heredity. A, C, G, and T represent groups of atoms. These are joined together in two, intercoiled chains (solid lines), with weak connections between them (dotted lines). The chains are complementary (A is paired with T, C with G). They are many thousands to many billions of groups long. Bacterial cells contain one DNA molecule, the cells of higher organisms contain a number (e.g. an ordinary human cell has 23 pairs of molecules in a nucleus, and some smaller ones outside this). (A, C, G, and T include linking atoms; in many books these are shown separately.)

have the same kind of chemicals functioning as genes.[30] These comprise groups of atoms of four different types (labelled A, C, G, and T), linked together in two, long, intertwined chains (Fig. 2.3). Chemists call these "DNA molecules", and the groups in them "nucleotides". When a cell divides the two strands of a DNA molecule untwist, and each has a matching strand built on to it.

[30] See, e.g., Berg and Singer, *Dealing with Genes*, Chaps. 1–3.

The sequence of nucleotides in a DNA molecule provides a pattern for the production of proteins, which go on to regulate the production of other chemicals, and control the way an organism develops. The DNA molecules in an organism accordingly determine the characteristics of that organism (its particular anatomy and physiology). Different members of the same species have DNA molecules with slightly different sequences of nucleotides in them. Members of different species have molecules with bigger differences in sequence between them.

Geneticists have established that, when a DNA molecule undergoes a disturbance (e.g. when it is struck by high-energy radiation), a change in the sequence of nucleotides can take place. This can happen particularly in the course of cell division, when a molecule is untwisting, and having matching strands built on to it. If such a change occurs in the generation of a reproductive cell, the new sequence can be passed on to offspring. Changes in DNA can also take place when egg cells are fertilized (sections of DNA can be exchanged between molecules, and a cell can acquire more than the usual number of molecules). Most DNA changes are either neutral or harmful to an organism, but some can give it an advantage in the environment it is in, as in the case of the bacteria I cited earlier.[22]

Geneticists therefore have a good understanding of how small changes in organisms can take place. The problem is obtaining evidence that large changes can be produced by a succession of small ones. Geneticists have studied the DNA in different species, and while some of the differences can be explained on an evolutionary model, others are difficult to explain in this way, at least on present knowledge.

A simple example is shown in Table 2.3. This gives the number of pairs of nucleotides in the DNA molecules of different animals. The figures in this table show that there is little correlation between the number of nucleotides and evolutionary development. Amphibians have more nucleotides than reptiles, and reptiles have more than birds. While this is partly because the molecules in some species contain repetitive sequences (e.g. ATATAT ...) having no genetic function,[31] the figures show how

---

[22] Strickberger, *Genetics*, pp. 765–766.
[31] Berg and Singer, *Dealing with Genes*, pp. 138–141.

Table 2.3 **Number of pairs of nucleotides in the DNA molecules of various animals.**[a]

Animal		Number of pairs (billions)
fish	eel	1.0
	carp	1.6
amphibians	common frog	4.3
	crested newt	22.5
reptiles	alligator	2.5
	pilot snake	2.1
birds	sparrow	1.0
	chicken	1.3
mammals	mouse	2.5
	human	3.2

[a] Number in a haploid cell (a cell containing one set of DNA molecules in its nucleus; ordinary cells contain two sets). Calculated from data of Shapiro, "Deoxyribonucleic Acid Content Per Cell of Various Organisms", and Strickberger, *Genetics*, Fig. 4-6 and Table 4-1 (pp. 45, 47).

difficult a task geneticists face in providing a detailed explanation of genetic differences on an evolutionary model.

A second example is shown in Table 2.4. This gives the differences in sequence between the same protein in different animals. These differences will occur in the gene that provides the pattern for the production of this protein. The protein is one that is involved in the production of energy (cytochrome *c*). On a simple evolutionary model one would expect the differences in sequence to increase the further apart animals are in the series fish, amphibia, reptiles, and mammals. Table 2.4 shows, however, that they do not. This can be explained by disparate rates of mutation following the separation of types (e.g. a high rate along the line leading

Table 2.4   Percentage differences between the sequence of groups in the same protein (cytochrome *c*) in different animals.

	Carp	Bullfrog	Rattlesnake	Pigeon	Dog	Human
Carp	0	13	25	14	11	17
Bullfrog		0	23	12	12	17
Rattlesnake			0	17	20	13
Pigeon				0	9	12
Dog					0	11
Human						0

Data from Dayhoff, *Atlas of Protein Sequence and Structure*, Vol. 5, Matrix 1 (p. D-8).

to the rattlesnake), but it again shows how difficult a task evolutionary geneticists face.

Biochemist Michael Behe has recently pointed out that many biological systems (e.g. the eye, blood-clotting, the immune system) are chemically very complex, and require all the components to be present for the system to operate.[32] He argues that evolution by mutation and natural selection does not provide a mechanism by which all the components can be brought together at the same time. Michael Denton agrees,[33] though he also observes that, as mutations in DNA can take place that have no effect on an organism, a series of such mutations could occur until one more mutation brings them all into play, and they combine to produce a new physiological function.[29]

Other mechanisms

Big mutations. Some biologists have explained the gaps in the fossil

---

[32] Behe, *Darwin's Black Box: The Biochemical Challenge to Evolution.*
[33] Denton, *Nature's Destiny*, Chap. 14.
[29] Denton, *Nature's Destiny*, pp. 278–279.

record by the occurrence of large genetic changes.[34] Geneticists have established that, under some conditions, sections of DNA can move from one molecule to another.[35] Movements of this kind could generate big mutations. One possibility is that sections of DNA in DNA-containing viruses could have become incorporated into the DNA of organisms at some stages of earth history.

Guided evolution. Some scientists have suggested that there are factors operating in biological systems guiding genetic changes and the course of evolution.[36] Possible factors are the natural tendency of biochemicals to behave in some ways and not others (cf. Sect. 2.3), and scientific laws operating at a higher level than the laws of chemistry and physics, governing the behaviour of biological systems as a whole. More work is needed to identify these factors, and to show how they have played a part in evolution. Michael Denton now favours a theory of this type (*Nature's Destiny*).

Evolution from space. Cosmologists Fred Hoyle and Chandra Wickramasinghe have estimated that the chances of organisms evolving on earth in the time available for this (Table 2.2) are very low, and have suggested that life partly evolved in space, and then came to earth (cf. Sect. 2.3).[37] They have also suggested that viruses from space became involved in evolution on earth in the manner indicated above. However, John Maynard Smith has calculated that there has been sufficient time for organisms to have evolved on earth.[38]

---

[34] Goldschmidt, *The Material Basis of Evolution*; Løvtrup, *Darwinism: The Refutation of a Myth.*

[35] Berg and Singer, *Dealing with Genes*, Chap. 8.

[36] E.g., Whyte, *Internal Factors in Evolution*; Rattray Taylor, *The Great Evolution Mystery*; Kauffman, *The Origins of Order*; *At Home in the Universe*; Goodwin, *How the Leopard Changed Its Spots*; McMenamin, *The Garden of Ediacara.* Cf. Lovelock, *Gaia: A New Look at Life on Earth*; Augros and Stanciu, *The New Biology*; Peacocke, *God and the New Biology* and other books; Davies, *The Cosmic Blueprint*; Corey, *Back to Darwin.*

[37] Hoyle and Wickramasinghe, *Evolution from Space* and other writings.

[38] Maynard Smith, *The Problems of Biology*, pp. 48–51.

2.5 Origin of human beings

According to the theory of evolution, human beings evolved from an early primate. Specific evidence for this is as follows:[39]

(1) Human remains appear late in the fossil record (Tables 2.1 and 2.2).

(2) Fossils have been found with features intermediate between those of apes and humans. Representative examples are shown in Figure 2.4. I have identified these by letter to avoid problems of classification.

(3) Human DNA is similar to that of apes. A great ape has 24 pairs of DNA molecules in the nucleus of an ordinary cell while a human has 23, with one pair resembling two of the former joined together. Nucleotide sequences are also similar. Those for chimpanzees and humans differ by only 1–2% (cf. Table 2.4).[40]

This evidence suffers similar problems to that for biological evolution generally. While most anthropologists regard at least some of the fossils in Figure 2.4 as transitional between apes and modern humans, there is considerable debate about which these are.[41] Classification is made difficult by the small number of specimens, the fact that many fossils are only fragmentary, and the variation that is possible within a species.[42]

Establishing ancestry is harder still. Even a recent DNA study is inconclusive. Researchers compared the sequences of nucleotides in a section of DNA from a Neanderthal fossil (type E) with the corresponding sequence in contemporary humans, and found that the average number of differences is greater than would be expected if modern humans evolved from Neanderthals.[43] Even so, the fossil's DNA is closer to some humans' than some humans' is to other humans'.[44]

---

[39] See, e.g., Jones, Martin, and Pilbeam (eds.), *The Cambridge Encyclopedia of Human Evolution*.

[40] Andrews and Stringer, "The Primates' Progress", p. 226.

[41] Reader, *Missing Links*; Andrews and Stringer, "The Primates' Progress", pp. 230–231; Gibbons, "A New Face for Human Ancestors".

[42] Clark, *The Fossil Evidence for Human Evolution*, Chap. 1.

[43] Krings and others, "Neandertal DNA Sequences and the Origin of Modern Humans".

[44] The sequence in the fossil differs from contemporary human sequences at 22–36 points, depending on the human, while the human sequences differ among themselves at 1–24 points. The averages (27.2 and 8.0 respectively) differ by a factor of 3.4, but the ranges overlap.

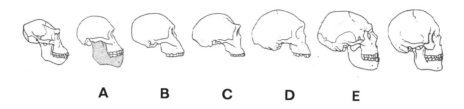

A   B   C   D   E

Figure 2.4   Fossil skulls compared with the skulls of a chimpanzee (left) and modern human (right) arranged in order of age. The jaw of A is modelled on other specimens. The ages have been estimated by various methods.

A: Sterkfontein 5, *ca.* 2.5 million years old
B: KNM-ER 1470, *ca.* 2 million years old
C: KNM-ER 3733, *ca.* 1.5 million years old
D: from Broken Hill, *ca.* 300,000 years old
E: Shandidar 1, *ca.* 60,000 years old

(From Jones, Martin, and Pilbeam, *The Cambridge Encyclopedia of Human Evolution.*)

Again, while the genetic differences between humans and apes are small in relative terms, they are nevertheless considerable. A 1–2% difference corresponds to millions of pairs of nucleotides (cf. Table 2.3).

Some human abilities are difficult to explain by the theory of evolution. For example, art and music do not seem to give human beings an advantage in what Darwin called "the struggle for life", and unselfish acts would seem to give them a disadvantage. Evolutionists respond to this difficulty by arguing that the ability of humans to do these things either does give them an advantage, or else is a by-product of abilities that do (i.e. humans have evolved with new capabilities X and Y, of which X has helped them to survive, and Y has been carried along with it).[45] However, even some

[45] Dawkins, *The Selfish Gene* and other writings; Ruse, *Evolutionary Naturalism*; Ferrière, "Help and You Shall Be Helped", Nowak and Sigmund, "Evolution of Indirect Reciprocity by Image Scoring". Cf. Crick, *The Astonishing Hypothesis*.

secular scientists have difficulty accepting that all human behaviour is biologically determined.[46]

Steve Jones, a leading geneticist and one of the editors of *The Cambridge Encyclopedia of Human Evolution*, has summed up the evidence for the evolution of humans as follows:[47]

> The evidence for human evolution is, in fact, still extraordinarily weak ... There are no more fossils than would cover a decent-sized table and we know almost nothing about what propelled a hairy and rather stupid ape into a bald and mildly intellectual human being.

He goes on to say that he nevertheless believes that humans have evolved because of the evidence for evolution in other animals, which I discussed in the last section (2.4).

Details of human evolution

Some anthropologists have argued that human beings evolved in many regions of the world, with sufficient interbreeding between populations to maintain a single species. This theory is based on the widespread distribution of fossils of type C, followed by D or E.

However, most anthropologists now believe that modern humans evolved in Africa about 200,000 years ago. A population migrated into the Middle East about 100,000 years ago, and then into other parts of the world, replacing types D and E in these places.[48]

This theory is based partly on fossil evidence, and partly on genetic studies of humans today. These show that the genetic variation among humans is much less than for other animals, and that the variation for African races is greater than for non-African ones. The first observation is consistent with a single origin in the relatively recent past, and the second with Africa as the location of this, the African races having had

---

[46] Rose, Lewontin, and Kamin, *Not in Our Genes*.
[47] Jones, "Why a Big Bang is Best Evidence of an Open Mind".
[48] Stringer and McKie, *African Exodus*.

longer for their genes to change. From the genetic variations, dates can be calculated for the origin of modern humans and the separation of non-African races. The calculations assume a constant mutation rate, and employ an estimate for this.

However, the evidence for an African origin is not conclusive. Human fossils are sparse and difficult to differentiate. Genetic variation can become small when populations come under pressure and then build up again. Mutation rates can vary (there could be more genetic variation among Africans because rates were higher in Africa for some reason). Modern humans could have evolved outside Africa, migrated there, and then a population migrated out.

Social evolution

Many anthropologists and sociologists extend the theory of evolution to society, morality, and religion. However, while some evidence may seem to support this, other evidence is against it.[49] For example, the "new morality" adopted by Western society in the 1960s is little different from the morality of the ancient Egyptians and Canaanites (Lev. 18). Moreover, it is inferior to the morality it replaced, as results now show. I shall exclude social evolution from my consideration of evolution in this book.

2.6 Alternative sciences

Progressive creation science

In the foregoing sections I have considered the orthodox scientific account of origins. Some Biblical Christian scientists, however, believe that this account is wrong, that there are specific signs of "intelligent design" in nature, and that these indicate that God intervened in the development of the universe at various stages.[50] They argue, for example, that chemical evolution is so improbable, and living organisms so evidently designed, that a more plausible explanation of the origin of life is that God created

---

[49] For a full discussion, see, e.g., Midgley, *Evolution as a Religion.*
[50] See, e.g., Moreland (ed.), *The Creation Hypothesis.*

the first organisms supernaturally, and placed them on the earth. Likewise, he introduced major new types of organism supernaturally.

Literal Biblical creation science

Some Biblical Christian scientists go further and argue that scientific observations are best explained by the Biblical account of origins, taken literally (Chap. 4).[51] Their case rests partly on weaknesses in the orthodox scientific account, and partly on more distinctive arguments. These include the following.

Evidence for a young earth

Henry Morris and others have presented a series of arguments, based on orthodox science, that the earth is only a few thousand years old.[52] For example, from the quantity of nickel salts entering the oceans through rivers each year, and the total quantity of these salts in the oceans, Morris has calculated that the earth cannot be more than about 9,000 years old.[53] The earth would be even younger if there were nickel salts in the oceans to start with, or if nickel salts are entering the oceans in other ways.

However, these arguments have failed to convince most orthodox scientists,[54] including Biblical Christian ones.[55] For example, in the above calculation Morris assumes that nickel salts are not being deposited from the oceans, whereas large quantities of such salts (albeit mostly from underwater springs) are being deposited in sediments and nodules on the

[51] See, e.g., Morris (ed.), *Scientific Creationism*; Morris and Parker, *What Is Creation Science?*; Brown, *In the Beginning*; Brand, *Faith, Reason, and Earth History*; Andrews, *From Nothing to Nature* and other writings; White, *What about Origins?* and other books; Croft, *How Life Began*; Bowden, *Science vs Evolution* and other books; Rosevear, *Creation Science*; Collyer, *Creation, Evolution and Science*; Peet, *In the Beginning, GOD Created ... .* See also Kelly, *Creation and Change*; McIntosh, *Genesis for Today*.

[52] Morris (ed.), *Scientific Creationism*, 1st edn., pp. 149–160; Morris and Parker, *What Is Creation Science?*, 2nd edn., pp. 273–293; Bowden, *True Science Agrees with the Bible*, Sect. 4.

[53] Morris, *Scientific Creationism*, 1st edn., p. 153.

[54] E.g., Stansfield, *The Science of Evolution*, pp. 80–84. Compare, however, Milton, *The Facts of Life*, Chap. 5.

[55] E.g., Young, *Christianity and the Age of the Earth*, Chaps. 8 and 9; Johnson, *Genesis, Geology and Catastrophism*, pp. 70–77; Van Till, Young, and Menniga, *Science Held Hostage*, Chaps. 3–5.

ocean floors.[56] Morris quotes figures for uranium salts which suggest that more of these are entering the oceans than are being deposited from them,[57] but this is because the rate of influx is inflated by the use of phosphate fertilisers, which contain traces of such salts.[58]

More difficult to answer is the argument that, if radioactive rocks have been giving off helium for billions of years, there ought to be more helium in the atmosphere than there is.[59] Helium is escaping from the atmosphere thermally, but not at a high enough rate. The generally accepted explanation is that helium is also escaping in a polar wind, but this has not been proved.[60]

Relative time

According to the theory of relativity two observers see the same events on different time scales if they are moving in relation to each other or are in different gravitational fields. Days on one time scale can correspond to millions of years on the other if the relative speed of the observers, or the difference in gravitational fields, is very high.

Gerald Schroeder has used this result to explain the different time scales of the Big Bang and Genesis.[61] However, his explanation requires God to have had a particular motion in relation to the earth when he created Adam, or to have been in a particular gravitational field. This seems contrived. Russell Humphreys has used a similar approach to explain how there could be starlight on earth if the universe was created a few thousand years ago (starlight usually takes a long time to travel to the earth).[62]

Decrease in speed of light

Orthodox scientists assume that the speed of light in a vacuum is a

---

[56] See, e.g., Goldberg, "The Processes Regulating the Composition of Sea Water"; Libes, *An Introduction to Marine Biogeochemistry*.
[57] Morris and Parker, *What Is Creation Science?*, 2nd edn., pp. 283–284.
[58] Bloch, "Some Factors Controlling the Concentration of Uranium in the World Ocean".
[59] Cf. Johnson, *Genesis, Geology and Catastrophism*, p. 71.
[60] Hunten, "Escape of Atmospheres, Ancient and Modern".
[61] Schroeder, *Genesis and the Big Bang*, Chap. 2.
[62] Humphreys, *Starlight and Time*.

constant. Barry Setterfield has pointed out, however, that measured values have decreased since the first was made 300 years ago (Fig. 2.5).[63] He infers from this that there is a difference between the time scale of "atomic" processes (e.g. radioactive decay, big bang) and "dynamical" ones (e.g. rotation of the earth, swing of a pendulum). He calculates that a 10–15 billion year date for the big bang on the first scale corresponds to about 5300–5700 B.C. on the second. However, the downward trend in measured values (0.3% in 300 years) is comparable with the uncertainty in the earlier measurements, and tails off as measurements become more accurate.

A secular cosmologist has attributed the reddening of light from distant galaxies to a decrease in the speed of light over time.[64] However, his model has only one time scale, and gives the age of the universe as 5–7 billion years.[65]

Flood geology

John Whitcomb and Henry Morris have argued that most of the strata in the earth's crust were laid in the flood described in Genesis 6–9 and its aftermath.[66] They take this flood to have been global (cf. Chap. 4). They explain the distribution of fossils by arguing that:

- ruptures in the ocean floors (Gen. 7:11) would have killed and buried sea creatures at an early stage;
- low-lying land habitats would have been flooded before those higher up;
- less mobile animals would have been drowned before more mobile ones;
- physical sorting of animal and vegetable remains would have taken place in the running water;

---

[63] Norman and Setterfield, "The Atomic Constants, Light, and Time". See also Bowden, *True Science Agrees with the Bible*, App. 1.

[64] Troitskii, "Physical Constants and Evolution of the Universe". Cf. Norman and Setterfield, pp. 57–59.

[65] Calculated from his function $c(t) = c_0(t_0/t)^{1/2}$.

[66] Whitcomb and Morris, *The Genesis Flood*.

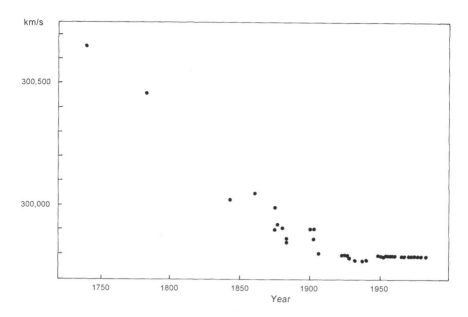

Figure 2.5   Measured values of the velocity of light in a vacuum (kilometres per second; after Norman and Setterfield, "The Atomic Constants, Light, and Time", Fig. 3, p. 53).

- major global disturbances would have continued after the flood.

However, this theory has won little acceptance among professional geologists,[67] including Biblical Christian ones.[68] They contend that

- many features of sedimentary rocks cannot be explained in the above way (e.g. sequences of strata containing fossils differing in only small details; alternating strata of different materials such as sand and clay);

---

[67] E.g., Ager, *The Nature of the Stratigraphical Record*, p. 32; *The New Catastrophism*, p. xi.
[68] E.g., Young, *Creation and the Flood*, and other books; Fraser, "The Age of the Earth"; Boardman, "Did Noah's Flood Cover the Entire World? — No"; Johnson, *Genesis, Geology and Catastrophism*. Compare, however, Austin, "Did Noah's Flood Cover the Entire World? — Yes".

- erosion and breakdown of igneous rocks, even under violent conditions, are too slow to have produced the material for most of the sedimentary rocks in the short period proposed by the theory;
- radiometric dating of volcanic layers in sedimentary rocks (Sect. 2.2) gives dates spread over millions of years;
- the detailed relationships between rocks in different regions of the world imply a long history of crustal development, with many major floods.

Anti-evolutionary scientists have sought to counter these objections by arguing, for example, that[69]

- most of the strata formed in the Genesis flood were produced, not by sedimentation, but by crystallization from mineral-rich hot water from underwater springs (cf. Gen. 7:11);
- radiometric dating is either flawed, or affected by changes in the speed of light, making years at the time of the Genesis flood appear like millions of years;
- only the lower strata in the earth's crust (below either the Tertiary or the Permian as classified in Table 2.1) were laid in the flood, subsequent events producing the upper strata.

However, Malcolm Bowden acknowledges that a "large gap ... still exists in the correlation of the Biblical account with the record of the rocks".

I discuss the Genesis flood further in Chapters 4 and 5.

---

[69] See Bowden, *True Science Agrees with the Bible*, App. 4.

3 Biblical account of origins

The Biblical account of origins is given in the early chapters of the book of Genesis. In this chapter and the next, I shall briefly discuss the text and authorship of Genesis, and the meaning of the early chapters.

3.1 Text

The standard Hebrew text of Genesis is the one established by Jewish scholars (the Masoretes) between about 500 and 1000 A.D., and referred to as the Masoretic text (MT). This comprises consonants (e.g. הר , *hr*) and signs to indicate how the text should be read (e.g. הַר , *har*, a hill or mountain). The latter were added by the Masoretes on the basis of oral tradition. However, there are few places where the text can be read in any other way.

The MT is a very late text, but there are good grounds for believing that it accurately preserves a much earlier one.[1] Firstly, the MT agrees very closely with fragments of Genesis found among the Dead Sea Scrolls, dating from about the 1st century B.C. Secondly, there is a close correspondence between the MT and two earlier versions — a Greek translation made in the 3rd century B.C. (the Septuagint, LXX), and a Samaritan revision dating from about the 5th century B.C. Thirdly, the Jews were commanded not to add to or subtract from their Scriptures (Deut. 4:1–2, 12:32), and there is good evidence that scribes took this seriously. Josephus, a Jewish historian in the 1st century A.D., wrote:[2]

> We have given practical proof of our reverence for our own Scriptures. For, although such long ages have now passed, no

---

[1] Wenham, *Genesis 1–15*, pp. xxiv–xxv.
[2] *Against Apion* 1:42–43 (Loeb edn.).

one has ventured either to add, or to remove, or to alter a syllable; and it is an instinct with every Jew, from the day of his birth, to regard them as the decrees of God, to abide by them, and, if need be, cheerfully to die for them. Time and again ere now the sight has been witnessed of prisoners enduring tortures and death in every form in the theatres, rather than utter a single word against the laws and the allied documents.

When the Jews went through religious declension, they did not so much change their Scriptures as neglect them (Judg. 21:25, 2 Kgs. 22:1–13). Devout Jews managed to preserve "the book of the law" during the captivity in Babylon (Neh. 8:1).

3.2 Authorship

Scholars are divided over the authorship of Genesis. The traditional view is that the first five books of the Bible (the Pentateuch) were written by Moses, or by someone very close to him using material that he supplied. This view is supported internally (Exod. 24:4, 7; Num. 33:2; Deut. 31:9, 24–26), and was endorsed by Jesus (Luke 24:44, John 5:46–47).

This view has been challenged on two grounds. First, there are some references in the books that suggest a later authorship. For example, the city of Leshem or Laish is called Dan in Genesis 14:14 even though it did not acquire this name until after the time of Moses (Josh. 19:47, Judg. 18:29). However, these references could be the result of scribes updating the text, without changing its essential meaning.[3]

Secondly, some scholars claim that there are linguistic differences between different sections of the Pentateuch (e.g. different names are used for God).[4] On the basis of these they postulate that the Pentateuch comprises four different versions of the early history of the Jews (designated J, E, P, and D), which were later combined into a single account by editors (R). For example, they attribute Genesis 1:1–2:3 to P, 2:4a to R, and 2:4b–3:24 to J.

---

[3] Kidner, *Genesis*, pp. 15–16.
[4] Skinner, *Genesis*.

Table 3.1   Documentary analysis of Genesis 7:10–8:14 describing the Flood.[a]

7:10	J	7:17b	J	8:2b–3a	J
7:11	P	7:18–21	P	8:3b–5	P
7:12	J	7:22–23a	J	8:6–12	J
7:13–16a	P	7:23b	R	8:13a	P
7:16b	J	7:23c	J	8:13b	J
7:17a	P	7:24–8:2a	P	8:14	P

[a] After Wenham, *Genesis 1–15*, p. 167.

However, the linguistic differences on which the hypothesis is based are questionable (e.g. the use of different names for God, as if an author would never use more than one name in a piece of writing). Also, some of the conclusions reached are very improbable (e.g. that the passage describing the Flood has the composition shown in Table 3.1). The case for the hypothesis is therefore unconvincing.[5]

3.3   Sources

If Moses was the author of Genesis, he could have obtained much of the material for it from his family. The series of genealogies in Genesis suggest that the ancient Hebrews kept details of their family history, and passed them on from one generation to another. This could have included an account of creation if God had revealed this to one of them. Alternatively, Moses could have obtained this from God, who spoke to him in a special way (Exod. 33:7–11; Num. 12:1–10).

However, many modern scholars believe that the author or authors of Genesis used material from pagan sources. Several pagan accounts of creation and a flood have been discovered in the Middle East, the original

[5] Cf. Kidner, *Genesis*, pp. 16–22.

versions of which scholars date from before Moses.[6] These accounts show some resemblances to Genesis, but differ from it in being polytheistic (Box 3.1). Scholars argue that the author or authors of Genesis used these accounts, and recast them in monotheistic form.

Box 3. 1

Babylonian creation epic (*Enūma eliš*)[a]

This begins with Apsu, the god of fresh water, and Tiamat, the goddess of sea water, as all that exists. Apsu and Tiamat give birth to other gods. These make such a noise that Apsu decides to do away with them. They get to hear about this, and one of them, Ea, kills him. Tiamat is disturbed by this, and some of the gods, led by Kingu, induce her to seek revenge. Ea's son, Marduk, succeeds in overcoming her, splitting her in two. From her two parts he makes the sky and the earth, and creates stations in the sky for the gods (the stars, moon, and sun). To relieve the gods from menial tasks he creates mankind from the blood of Kingu. The gods thank him by building the city of Babylon and a temple to him there, and acclaim him as their king.

[a] Heidel, *The Babylonian Genesis*; Pritchard (ed.), *Ancient Near Eastern Texts*, pp. 60–72.

However, the reverse process could equally well have taken place: the authors of the pagan accounts could have been informed by Hebrew tradition. The absence of any record of the latter prior to Genesis does not mean that the ancient Hebrews did not have a tradition, or that this did not influence their neighbours. Their unsettled history did not lend itself to the preservation of artefacts in the way in which the more settled histories of some of their neighbours did.

Furthermore, the crude polytheism of the pagan accounts compared with the elevated monotheism of the Hebrew version of events strongly

---

[6] Pritchard (ed.), *Ancient Near Eastern Texts*.

suggests that the former have been obtained by corruption of the latter rather than the latter by refinement of the former. Stories are more often corrupted than refined.[7]

For Christians, the issue is settled by Jesus in Matthew 19:4–5. Here he states that the author of Genesis 2:24 is God himself: "*the Creator ... said*, 'For this reason a man will leave his father and mother and be united to his wife ...'".

3.4 Genesis in the rest of the Bible

Later Biblical authors took Genesis to be authoritative. For example, Jesus based his teaching on divorce on it, in the passage from which I have just quoted (Mat. 19:3–12). I shall discuss this in a later chapter (Chap. 8).

---

[7] Kitchen, *Ancient Orient and Old Testament*, p. 89.

4 Literal meaning of Genesis

In this chapter I shall discuss the literal meaning of Genesis.[1] Whether or not the author intended that it should be taken literally I shall discuss later (Chap. 7).

Genesis 1: Creation

Genesis 1 describes the creation of the universe ("the heavens and the earth"), by God, in six days. The days are indicated by the phrase, "there was evening and there was morning, one day/a second day/a third day etc." (vv. 5, 8, 13, etc.).

The beginning

Whether God created the universe from nothing (*ex nihilo*) or starting from a primitive earth is not clear. The word translated "create" (*bārā'*) does not necessarily imply creation from nothing (compare 1:27 with 2:7), and the Hebrew of verses 1–3 can be read either way.[2] However, later Biblical writers take the creation to have been from nothing (Prov. 8:22–31, Heb. 11:3). On this reading, verse 1 (lit. "In [a] beginning God created the heavens and the earth") describes the creation of a primitive universe, verse 2 ("And/Now the earth was …") the condition of the earth at this stage, and verse 3 the next development.

There are hints in the narrative (the absence of the definite article before "beginning"; the plurals "Let us make" and "like one of us" in 1:26 and 3:22, cf. 1 Kgs. 22:19, Job 38:4–7, etc.) that the author did not

---

[1] Cf. Kidner, *Genesis*; Wenham, *Genesis 1–15*; Hamilton, *Genesis 1–17*.
[2] Wenham, *Genesis 1–15*, pp. 11–13; Hamilton, *Genesis 1–17*, pp. 103–108.

regard the creation of the universe as the beginning of everything. Jesus spoke of a time "before the world was" (John 17:5, 24).

As described in verse 2, the primitive earth was bare, dark, and covered with water (verses 9–10 indicate that it was completely covered).[3] Many commentators assume that it was chaotic, but there is no necessary implication of this. Some translate verse 2 "And/But the earth *became* desolate and empty", and argue that verses 3–31 describe a fresh creation out of the ruins of an earlier one (the "gap" theory). However, most Hebrew scholars reject this interpretation, the construction being identical to that elsewhere rendered "Now X was ..." (e.g. 3:1, Jon. 3:3).[4]

Some commentators point out that the Hebrew word *hā'āreṣ* (*hā* + *'ereṣ*, "the earth") refers to the earth as it was conceived at the time, not as we know it today. However, the latter is implied by the scale of subsequent events (the creation of light, vv. 3–5; of the sky, vv. 6–8; of the sun, moon, and stars, vv. 14–19). The suggestion that *hā'āreṣ* means "the land" (as in 12:1 etc.)[5] is precluded for the same reason.

Order of creation

The author gives the order of creation as follows:

Day 1:	? Primitive universe (vv. 1–2)
	Light, day and night (vv. 3–5)
Day 2:	Sky (vv. 6–8)
Day 3:	Dry land (vv. 9–10)
	Vegetation (vv. 11–13)
Day 4:	Sun, moon, and stars (vv. 14–19)
Day 5:	Large long-bodied animals (*tannînim*)[6]

---

[3] Cf. Tsumura, *The Earth and the Waters in Genesis 1 and 2*.

[4] Kidner, *Genesis*, p. 44: Blocher, *In the Beginning*, pp. 41–43; Hamilton, *Genesis 1–17*, pp. 115–116.

[5] Sailhamer, *Genesis Unbound*.

[6] Cf. Psa. 148:7.

Aquatic and flying animals (vv. 20–23)

Day 6:   Land animals (vv. 24–25)

Human beings (vv. 26–31)

This order differs from the scientific one discussed in Chapter 2 (the earth is created before the sun and the stars, seed-bearing plants before aquatic forms of life, birds before small, non-*tannîn* reptiles). Scholars have attempted to bring Genesis 1 into line with the scientific order,[7] but their explanations strain the Hebrew text. For example, some take verses 14–19 to mean that the sun, moon, and stars "came into view" on day 4 — the earth having been shrouded in water vapour until green plants appeared, as on the scientific picture. However, there is nothing in the Hebrew to support this reading.[8] The same applies to the suggestion that the sun, moon, and stars were "completed" on day 4. Likewise, *deše'* in verses 11–12 cannot refer to algae: verse 11 literally reads, "And God said, let the earth shoot (<*dāšā'*) shoots (*deše'*), plant[s] seeding seed, tree[s] of fruit making fruit …".

Some commentators have suggested that the author chose the order in Genesis 1 to counter pagan ideas about the cosmos. Many ancient peoples worshipped the sun, moon, and stars as gods (cf. Box 3.1). To emphasize that they are not gods the author relegated their creation to day 4. However, it is one thing to argue that the author wanted to counter pagan errors, it is another to conclude that he did this by changing the order of creation. He could have addressed the problem directly, as in the command not to worship the sun, moon, and stars in Deuteronomy 4:19.

The "days"

Commentators interpret the "days" in various ways:

(1) as successive periods of 24 hours during which God created the universe;

---

[7] E.g., Rendle Short, *Modern Discovery and the Bible*, Chap. 4; Pearce, *Who Was Adam?*, Chap 11; *Evidence for Truth*, Vol. 1, Chap. 1; Young, *Creation and the Flood*, Chap. 6; Newman and Eckelmann, *Genesis One and the Origin of the Earth*, Chap. 5.

[8] Blocher, *In the Beginning*, pp. 45–46.

(2) as representing long periods of time or intervals in God's time (cf. Job 10:5, Psa. 90:4, 2 Pet. 3:8) during which he created the universe;[9]

(3) as successive periods of 24 hours during which God revealed to the author how he had created the universe;[10]

(4) as successive periods of 24 hours during which God declared how he was going to make the universe before he started;[11]

(5) as periods of 24 hours, with long intervals between them, marking the beginning of each new phase in God's creative activity.[12]

Of these (1) receives the strongest support from the text. On day 1 God creates "day" and "night" (vv. 3–5). On day 4 he creates the sun and the moon to "rule over the day and the night" (vv. 16, 18), and to be "for signs, for seasons, for days and years" (v. 14). The implication is that on day 1 God established the cycle of daylight and darkness on the earth, and on day 4 created the sun to maintain this. There is little support for (3)–(5). (4) and (5) conflict with Exodus 20:11, "in six days the LORD made the heavens and the earth". (3) stretches the meaning of ʿasâ in this verse and Genesis 2:2–3, from "make" to "make known".

God's verdict

The author states that, at various stages during the creation, God looked at what he had made and judged it "good" (vv. 4, 10, 12, 18, 21, 25). At the end of the final stage he judged everything "very good" (v. 31). At this point all the land animals and human beings were vegetarian (vv. 29–30).

Day 7

The author states that, on day 7, God "ceased" (šābaṯ) from "all his work of creating which he had done" (2:1–3). In Exodus God told Moses that

---

[9] E.g., Rendle Short, *Modern Discovery and the Bible*, Chap. 4; Young, *Creation and the Flood*, Chap. 4; Spanner, *Biblical Creation and the Theory of Evolution*.

[10] Wiseman, *Creation Revealed in Six Days*.

[11] Hayward, *Creation and Evolution*.

[12] Newman and Eckelmann, *Genesis One and the Origin of the Earth*.

he "rested" (*nūaḥ*) and was "refreshed" (20:11, 31:17). This does not mean that he ceased from all activity in the world (cf. John 5:16–17).

For day 7, the author omits the phrase, "there was evening and there was morning". Some commentators take this to mean that day 7 is still proceeding, and argue from this that days 1–6 represent long periods of time [interpretation (2) above]. According to the New Testament, God's rest from "all his work of creating" is certainly still proceeding (Heb. 3:7–4:11). However, it is also possible that day 7 ended as usual, with God's rest from creating continuing on day 8, and that the author omitted "there was evening and there was morning, a seventh day" for a literary reason (e.g. to preserve the climax "God blessed the seventh day and hallowed it"). In 2:4 the writer uses "day" (*yôm*) to refer to a longer period than 24 hours, but this does not establish its meaning in Genesis 1.

Genesis 2 and 3: Adam and Eve, the Fall and the Curse

Genesis 2:1–3 completes Genesis 1 (see above). Genesis 2:4 (lit. "These are the generations of the heavens and the earth when they were created ...") introduces a new section.[13] The formula "These are the generations of ..." is used for this purpose throughout Genesis (5:1, 6:9, 10:1, etc.). It may be paraphrased "This is the history of ...".

Genesis 2 and 3 tell the following story:

2:4–6 Introduction. The state of the earth before God created man.

2:7 God created (lit.) "the man" (*hā* + *'āḏām*, as in 1:27) from "the dust of the ground". The man is called Adam from 4:25 (the definite article is retained, except after *lᵉ*, until 4:25).

2:8–15 God planted a garden for the man. This had in it "the tree of life" and "the tree of the knowledge of good and evil".

2:16–17 God commanded the man not to eat from the tree of the knowledge of good and evil, warning him that, if he does, he will die.

---

[13] Kidner, *Genesis*, pp. 23–24, 59; Wenham, *Genesis 1–15*, pp. 55–56; Hamilton, *Genesis 1–17*, pp. 2–10, 150–152.

2:18–25 God created a partner for the man out of one of his ribs. When the man saw her and the gap in his side, he declared her to be "bone of my bones, and flesh of my flesh". In 3:20 he names her Eve.

3:1–7 The snake or serpent (*hā* + *nāḥāš*) deceived the woman into eating fruit from the tree of the knowledge of good and evil and she gave some to the man.

3:8–13 God interrogated the man and the woman.

3:14–15 God condemned the serpent to living on its belly.

3:16 God condemned the woman to a harder life as a mother and wife.

3:17–19 God cursed the ground so that the man would find growing food much harder, and condemned him to death.

3:20–24 The sequel. God drove the man out of the garden, away from the tree of life, whose fruit would have kept him from dying.

The story has a grim ending. By denying Adam access to the tree of life, God condemned him and his descendants[14] to death (3:22–24). To compensate for this he made Eve bear more children (3:16, "I will greatly multiply/make very great your toil and your conception"[15]). He also killed animals to provide the couple with clothing as they had become aware of their nakedness (3:21, cf. 2:25, 3:7).

"Death" in the narrative means ceasing to live and returning to the ground (3:19, "dust you are, and to dust you shall return"): its opposite is living for ever (3:22, cf. 5:24). Some commentators argue that "death" must refer to spiritual death because Adam did not die physically "on the day" that he ate from the tree of the knowledge of good and evil (2:17). However, 2:17 can be understood: "on the day that you eat from it you shall surely eventually die" (= 3:19). Consistent with this, on the day Adam sinned, God denied him access to the tree that would have given him immortality (3:22–24). He changed Adam's life from one that would

---

14 Except Enoch and Elijah (Chap. 8, Sect. 8.1).

15 Many translations obscure the meaning of this verse, treating "toil and conception" as a hendiadys. On the meaning of the verb, see Blocher, *In the Beginning*, pp. 180–181. The word translated "toil" (*'iṣṣābôn*) is used also in 3:17 and 5:29.

not have ended in death to one that would (3:19) and did (5:5). The idiom in 2:17, lit. "in the day ... dying you shall die", is used in 1 Kings 2:37 in a similar way (there is an interval of some days between 2:40 and 2:46).

Some commentators argue that there must have been physical death before the Fall because, without it, the earth would have become overpopulated (cf. 1:28). However, this presupposes sustained reproduction. The narrative implies that, but for the Fall, Eve's conception would have been low (3:16 above).

Genesis 1, 2, and 3 are connected. Taken together they constitute a *theodicy* — they provide an explanation of how there can be evil in a world created by God. Genesis 1 affirms that there was no evil in the world when God created it — it was "very good" (1:31). Genesis 2 and 3 explain how evil came into it — through creatures abusing the freedom God had given them. God allowed them to commit their crimes, and only intervened after they had done so (3:8). He then punished them for what they had done, and changed the natural order to make their lives less pleasant for them. In particular, he cursed the ground, and brought death upon human beings.

Relation between Genesis 1 and 2

Many commentators argue that there are discrepancies between the accounts of creation in Genesis 1 and 2, and that Genesis 2 is from a different source to Genesis 1 (Chap. 3, Sects. 3.2 and 3.3), or describes the creation of a different race of human beings from Genesis 1.[16] However, it is possible to harmonize the accounts, such that Genesis 2 amplifies day 6 of Genesis 1, as detailed below. The author ties Genesis 2–4 to Genesis 1 in 5:1–3 (5:1b–2 summarizes 1:26–28 and 5:3 summarizes 4:25). Jesus linked 1:27 and 2:24 in Matthew 19:4–5.

Order of creation. According to Genesis 1, God made the flying animals on day 5 (1:20–23) and the land animals on day 6 (1:24–25), followed by man (1:26–31). According to Genesis 2, as usually translated,

[16] Pearce, *Who Was Adam?* and other writings; Fischer, *The Origins Solution.*

he made man first (2:7), and then the land animals and flying animals (2:19). However, this inconsistency can be resolved by translating 2:19 as a pluperfect, "Now the LORD God *had* formed every beast of the field and[17] every bird of the sky".[18] Hebrew verbs do not indicate the time of an action: this is determined by idiom and context. The construction here is unusual for a pluperfect,[19] but other examples are known (Exod. 33:5; Num. 1:48; Judg. 2:6; 1 Sam. 14:24, 17:13; 1 Kgs. 13:12 MT; Isa. 38:21, 22; Dan.1:9).

State of the earth when man created. Genesis 2:4–7 could be taken to mean that when God created man there was no vegetation, in contradiction to Genesis 1, where God created vegetation on day 3 (1:11–13) and man on day 6 (1:26–31). However, the state of the earth described in 2:5–6 ("... the LORD God had not sent rain on the earth... but a stream[20] came up from the earth and watered the whole surface of the ground") corresponds to the one presented in 1:2, before God made the clouds (1:6–8) and dry land (1:9–10).[21] On this reading 2:5–6 reminds the reader of the state of the earth when God started creating (2:4b), and 2:7 picks up the account of creation on day 6.

Number of human beings created. As usually translated Genesis 1:26–28 seems to speak of the creation of many human beings, whereas Genesis 2 describes the creation of one man, and from him, one woman. However, the wording of 1:27, with its definite article (as in 2:7) and switch from singular to plural (lit. "God created the man...male and female he created them"), correlates with the account in Genesis 2, and allows the plurals in 1:26–28 to be identified with Adam and Eve. Compare also 5:1–2.

---

[17] Or: "in addition to" (the omission of the first '*ēṯ* makes the construction like that of 1 Kings 11:1).

[18] Kline, "Genesis", p. 84; Hamilton, *Genesis* 1–17, p.176.

[19] Driver, *Hebrew Tenses*, Sect. 76, *Obs.*

[20] Hebrew '*ēḏ*, used only here and in Job 36:27. The Septuagint translates the word "spring" here but "cloud" in Job 36:27, whence the traditional rendering "mist". However, the wording of Genesis 2:6 favours "spring", and this is supported by etymological considerations (Tsumura, *The Earth and the Waters in Genesis 1 and 2*). Its use in Job 36:27 could be poetic, a cloud being a source of water like a spring.

[21] Cf. Kidner, *Genesis*, pp. 59–60.

Naming of the animals. Some commentators argue that Adam could not have named every kind of animal (2:19–20) within a few hours on day 6. However, he could have employed a simple classification of animals, as the narrator himself does (3:1, *nāḥāš*, "snake"). Adam's cry "at last" (*hā* + *pa'am*, "this time") when he sees Eve (2.23) need not mean that the naming took a long time: it could relate to the succession of those brought before him (*pa'am* is not used exclusively of time, e.g. Num. 14:22).

Eden

The location of Eden is a puzzle.[22] The narrator states that it is "in the east", i.e. east of Canaan (2:8). This points to Mesopotamia as a possible location (Fig. 4.1). Mesopotamia, however, is not mentioned (contrast 11:2).

The narrator also gives the location as the area in which the rivers Pishon, Gihon, Hiddekel (Tigris), and Euphrates have their headwaters (2:10–14). The first two rivers cannot be identified, but the Tigris and Euphrates have their headwaters in the highlands north of Mesopotamia (Fig. 4.1). However, Havilah and Cush, the countries round which the Pishon and Gihon flow, are identified elsewhere in the Old Testament as north-eastern Arabia (Gen. 25:18, 1 Sam. 15:7) and Ethiopia (Ezek. 29:10) respectively, south of Mesopotamia.

A reasonable solution to this problem is to focus on the Tigris and Euphrates, whose identification is certain. Anyone knowing these rivers would have at least a general idea where they flowed from. This places Eden on the highland plateau north of Mesopotamia. The Pishon and Gihon are then two of the other rivers that have their headwaters in this area, and Havilah and Cush are different from Havilah and Cush elsewhere in the Old Testament. Slight support for this is that *ḥ*ᵃ*wîlâ* carries the definite article in 2:11 (*haḥ*ᵃ*wîlâ*) but not elsewhere.

Some commentators try to resolve the puzzle by suggesting that the narrator is describing the river system in an upstream direction. They

---

[22] Driver, *Genesis*, pp. 57–60; Kidner, *Genesis*, pp. 63–64; Wenham, *Genesis 1–15*, pp. 66–67. See also Rohl, *A Test of Time*, Vol. 2, Chap. 1.

identify the river in Eden (2:10) as the Persian Gulf, and the "heads" as river mouths. The Assyrians called the Gulf a river (*nar marratum*, "bitter river"), and the upper layer of water in a sea can be fresh near river estuaries (fresh water is lighter than sea water). However, the narrative ("a river went out of Eden to water the garden, and from there it divided") reads like a downstream description, and the watering of Paradise by a river later called "bitter" seems unlikely.[23]

The Serpent

Most commentators take the Serpent to be, or to symbolize, or to be in thrall to, the Devil. However, there is nothing in the passage to indicate this.[24] The author refers to him throughout by the ordinary word for a snake (*nāḥāš*), and describes him as one of the animals which God had made (3:1). The author nowhere states that he is inherently evil, only "clever" (*'ārûm*, 3:1), a word that can have a good or bad sense (e.g. Job 5:12, Prov. 12:16). What the Serpent does is misuse his cleverness. He beguiles Eve with the very reasonable argument that eating from the tree of the knowledge of good and evil would not bring death, only knowledge of good and evil (3:1–5). Up to a point he was right — eating from the tree only had this effect. God had to drive Adam and Eve away from the tree of life to bring about their death (3:22–24). After the Curse, the snake becomes the animal we know, living on its belly, eating at ground level, menacing and being menaced by human beings (3:14–15).

In the New Testament, however, the Serpent *is* identified with the Devil (Rev. 12:9, 20:2, cf. John 8:44, 1 John 3:8). If Genesis 3 is understood literally, this means that the Serpent, having started off as one of the animals, *became* the Devil. Its spirit lived on after the death of its body, attaching itself to the angels, and marauding the earth (Job 1:6–7, 2:1–2, 1 Pet. 5:8, etc.). Its physical offspring, however, are the snakes we know (cf. Luke 10:18–19). The first hint of an evil spirit in Genesis is in 4:7, where Cain is warned that "sin is crouching at the door" (cf. 1 John 3:12).

[23] The Babylonian map of the world that some scholars cite (Driver, *Genesis*, p. 60, n. 1) looks symbolic. (For a photograph, see Ball, *Light from the East*, p. 23.)
[24] Cf. Hamilton, *Genesis 1–17*, pp. 187–188.

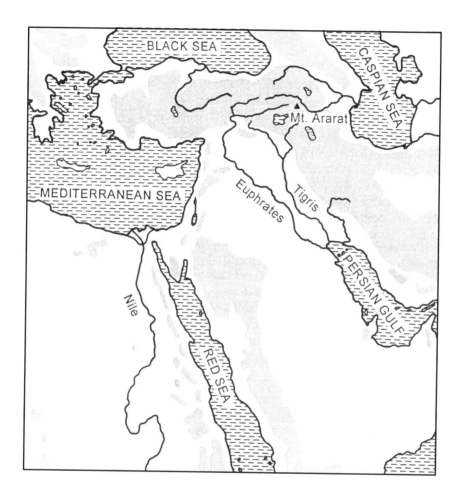

Figure 4.1   Map of the world known to the ancient Hebrews (Gen. 10), showing the main rivers, land over 1,000 metres or 3,000 feet (shaded), and the ancient shore-line of the Persian Gulf. Mesopotamia is the lowland area between the Tigris and Euphrates. The highlands north of Mesopotamia extend from modern Turkey, through Armenia, to Iran. (Based on Muir and Philip, *Philips' Atlas of Ancient and Classical History*.)

Many Christian commentators identify the Devil as a fallen angel, which posed as, or took possession of, the Serpent. This identification is based on Isaiah 14:12–15 and Ezekiel 28:13–17. However, the first prophecy concerns the king of Babylon (Isa. 14:4) and the second the king of Tyre (Ezek. 28:12).[25] The identification in any case misses the whole point of Genesis 3, that evil in the world originated *within* the world, and did not come in from outside. God created the world good, creatures misused their freedom and spoilt it. Genesis does refer to a fall of angels (if "sons of God" are angels as in Job 1:6, 2:1), but this does not come until 6:1–4, and describes quite different misconduct — angels leaving heaven to have affairs with women (cf. 2 Pet. 2:4, Jude 6).

Extent of the Curse

According to Genesis, the creation, before the Fall, was "very good" (1:31). After the Fall God cursed it — he condemned the Serpent to live on its belly (3:14–15), Eve to a difficult life (3:16), and Adam to toil and death (3:17–19). He told Adam, "Cursed is the ground because of you" (3:17), and explained that it would now produce thorns and thistles (3:18a).

Later Biblical writers amplify this. Firstly, they describe the creation as failing to fulfil its intended purpose (Eccl. 1:1–11, Rom. 8:20). They link this failure to the mortality of human beings (Eccl. 1:4, 11; Rom. 8:19–21), which renders even good aspects of nature futile (Eccl. 1:5–7). Secondly, they see creation as needing to be renewed, and look forward to a time when it will be (Psa. 102:25–26, Mat. 19:28, Acts 3:21), and there is "a new heaven and a new earth" (Isa. 65:17–25, 2 Pet. 3:13, Rev. 21:1–5), and "no more curse" (Rev. 22:1–5). Thirdly, they specify other aspects of the present order that are not "very good":

- physical disabilities (John 9:1–7 etc.);
- disease (Mat. 4:23–24 etc.);
- decay (Mat. 6:19–20 etc.);
- predation (Isa. 11:1–9 etc.);[26]

---

[25] Blocher, *In the Beginning*, p. 42.
[26] On Psalm 104:21, 24–28, compare Matthew 5:45.

- natural disasters (Mat. 24:7 etc.).

Biblical writers regard some physical disabilities, disease, and natural disasters as God's punishment for the sins of the individuals concerned (Exod. 7–12, 1 Cor. 11:27–32, etc.), or as the work of Satan in an individual's life (Job 1–2, Luke 13:10–16). However, Jesus made it clear that these evils can have a more general origin (John 9:1–3a, Luke 13:4–5). Commentators have traditionally taken this to be the Fall (cf. Milton's *Paradise Lost*). In Genesis predation certainly begins after this (6:11–12, see below; cf. 1:29–30), and in Revelation disease ends when there is "no more curse" (Rev. 22:2–3).

Biblical writers conclude that the creation now displays two qualities: the "eternal power and deity" of the one who made it (Psa. 104, Rom. 1:20), and "bondage of corruption" because of human sin (Rom. 8:20–23).

Death of animals

Commentators are divided over the question of whether the natural, non-violent death of animals should be included in the above list.[27] The strongest argument for excluding it is that Adam's immortality depended on him eating from the tree of life (Gen. 3:22–23) and there is no reference to animals eating from this tree. Henri Blocher also suggests that Adam would have needed to witness the death of animals to understand God's warning in 2:17, "you shall surely die".[28] However, God could have explained death to him in the same terms as in 3:19 ("dust you are, and to dust you shall return").

Reasons for including the death of animals in the above list are as follows:

- The author of Ecclesiastes describes the death of animals as futile (Eccl. 3:18–21). His argument (humans die as animals do and therefore human life is futile) indicates that he regarded the death

---

[27] Compare, e.g., Whitcomb and Morris, *The Genesis Flood*, App. 1, and Spanner, *Biblical Creation and the Theory of Evolution*, Chap. 6.

[28] Blocher, *In the Beginning*, p. 185.

of animals as being futile in itself, not just rendered futile by the death of humans (cf. above).

- The prophet Nathan told a story about a poor man whose one sheep was very precious to him. A rich man took the sheep and slaughtered it (2 Sam. 12:1–4). By implication, the poor man suffered a great loss. His loss would have been no less if, in the course of time, the sheep had died naturally.

- When Jonah complained that God had spared Nineveh from destruction, God told him, "should I not pity Nineveh, that great city, in which are more than a hundred and twenty thousand people ... and many cattle?" (Jon. 4:11). This implies that the lives of cattle are of value to God.

- Jesus taught that God watches over the death even of a sparrow (Mat. 10:29).

- Under the old covenant, animals were put to death in place of human beings, to atone (however ineffectually) for their sins (Lev. 16, etc.).

- Under the new covenant, Jesus is called "the Lamb of God who takes away the sin of the world" (John 1:29, etc.).

- John had a vision of heaven in which he saw four living creatures — one like a lion, one like a calf, one like a man, and one like an eagle (Rev. 4:6–8). These creatures presumably represent wild animals, domestic animals, human beings, and birds, and are immortal. Ezekiel had a similar vision (Ezek. 1:5–14).

These considerations suggest that Biblical authors regarded the death of at least higher animals as not being "very good", but part of the "bondage of corruption" of creation (Rom. 8:20–23).

Note that no distinction can be drawn between human beings and animals on the basis of the statement in Genesis 2:7 that God breathed into Adam "the breath of life" and Adam became "a living being". Genesis also describes animals as "living beings" (1:21, 24; 2:19; 9:10 etc.) having "the breath of the spirit of life" (7:22). The difference between human beings and animals is that human beings bear the image of God (1:26–27).

Note finally that Genesis distinguishes between animals and plants in describing only animals as having "the breath of the spirit of life" (7:22), and in allowing plants to be used for food from the beginning (1:29–30, cf. 9:2–4).

Genesis 4: Cain and Abel

Genesis 4 continues the story of Adam and Eve. They had two sons, Cain and Abel (vv. 1–2). Cain murdered Abel, fled to the east, and brought up his family there (vv. 3–24). His wife (v. 17) was presumably a sister (cf. 5:4b). Adam and Eve then had another son, Seth (vv. 25–26).

Cain expressed the fear that "anyone who finds me will kill me" (v. 14). This suggests that Abel too was married and had sons — who else would have wanted to "find" Cain and avenge Abel's murder (cf. Num. 35:9–28, 2 Sam. 14:4–7)?

Genesis 5: Adam to Noah

Genesis 5 gives the line of descent from Adam to Noah and his sons, including the age at which each named individual fathered the next one, and the age at which he died. The ages in the genealogy differ between the three ancient versions of the text (Hebrew, Samaritan, and Greek) as shown in Table 4.1. Most of the differences are of 100 years. Which version is original is difficult to decide.[29]

A feature of the genealogy is the long life-spans (e.g. Adam, 930 years). These are an integral part of the narrative: in 6:3 God declares that he will shorten the life-spans of human beings.[30] The long spans are not due to the use of a shorter year because the year of the Flood (when Noah was 600) is of about normal length (see below).

---

[29] Cf. Wenham, *Genesis 1–15*, pp. 130–133.

[30] Some commentators take the phrase "his days shall be a hundred and twenty years" to refer to the period between 6:3 and the Flood, but it more naturally refers to life-spans, which gradually fall after the Flood to a maximum of about 120 years (see Wenham, *Genesis 1–15*, p. 142).

Table 4.1   Genealogy from Adam to Noah (Genesis 5).[a]

		Age of fathering			Age at death		
		Heb.	Sam.	Gk.	Heb.	Sam.	Gk.
1.	Adam	130	130	230	930	930	930
2.	Seth	105	105	205	912	912	912
3.	Enosh	90	90	190	905	905	905
4.	Kenan	70	70	170	910	910	910
5.	Mahalalel	65	65	165	895	895	895
6.	Jared	162	62	162	962	847	962
7.	Enoch	65	65	165	365[b]	365[b]	365[b]
8.	Methuselah	187	67	167[c]	969	720	969
9.	Lamech	182	53	188	777	653	753
10.	Noah	500	500	500	950[d]	950[d]	950[d]

[a] Skinner, *Genesis*, p. 134. Ages in years.
[b] Age at translation (v. 24).
[c] Some manuscripts read 187.
[d] 9:29.

An important question is whether the genealogy is complete, for if it is, a chronology can be constructed by adding up the ages at which sons in the succession are fathered (Table 4.2). This question is difficult to answer. On the one hand, many genealogies in the Bible are selective, and use "A fathered B" to mean "A fathered the line that led to B" (e.g. Matthew 1:7–10 omits three names from the middle of 1 Chronicles 3:10–14).[31] On the other hand, the genealogy in this chapter is exceptional in giving the ages at which sons are fathered. This age could have had a non-chronological significance (like age at death, Prov. 9:10–11), but if it did, what this was can only be conjectured.

[31] Schaeffer, *No Final Conflict*, Chap. 4; cf. Albright, *New Horizons in Biblical Research*, p. 11, note 1.

Table 4.2 Chronology from Creation to the Flood if the genealogy in Genesis 5 is complete.[a]

	Heb.		Sam.		Gk.	
	b.	d.	b.	d.	b.	d.
Creation		0		0		0
Adam	–	930	–	930	–	930
Seth	130	1042	130	1042	230	1142
Enosh	235	1140	235	1140	435	1340
Kenan	325	1235	325	1235	625	1535
Mahalalel	395	1290	395	1290	795	1690
Jared	460	1422	460	1307	960	1922
Enoch	622	987[b]	522	887[b]	1122	1487[b]
Methuselah	687	1656	587	1307	1287	2256
Lamech	874	1651	654	1307	1454[c]	2207[c]
Noah	1056	2006	707	1657	1642[c]	2592[c]
Shem	1556		1207		2142[c]	
Flood[d]		1656		1307		2242[c]

[a] In years after Creation; b. = birth, d. = death.
[b] Year of translation.
[c] Or 20 years later (Table 4.1, note c).
[d] 7:6.

Ancient commentators are divided on the issue. The Jewish historian Josephus (1st century A.D.) took the genealogy to be complete, and constructed a chronology from it.[32] According to an early Armenian scholar, however, "Some used to say that there were innumerable aeons from Adam to Noah".[33] In the New Testament Jude distinguished Enoch in the genealogy from others bearing this name[34] (Gen. 4:17, 25:4, 46:9) by describing him as "the seventh from Adam" (Jude 14). This could indicate that he took the genealogy to be complete, but the identification only requires the list to be a standard one, which everybody knew.[35]

[32] *Jewish Antiquities* 1:82–88.
[33] Insertion in Philo's *Questions and Answers on Genesis* 1:87 (Loeb edn., p. 55, note *i*).
[34] Heb. $H^a n\hat{o}k$, Gk. *Enōch*, Engl. Hanoch or Enoch.
[35] Peter described Noah as "eighth" (2 Pet. 2:5), but he presumably meant "one of eight" (cf. 1 Pet. 3:20).

Note that, if the genealogy is complete, the best Greek manuscripts date Methuselah's death 14 years after the Flood (Table 4.2). However, this could be because the date of the Flood (when Noah was "600 years old", 7:6) is only approximate (all the figures for Noah look like round numbers).[36] Alternatively, the genealogy could be incomplete. For the translators to have introduced a discrepancy over Methuselah's death would have been very inept.

Note also that, if the genealogies are complete, there is considerable overlap between generations (in the Samaritan version Adam is still alive when Noah is 200!). However, this is a consequence of the long life-spans, and would arise in any society in which there is longevity.

Genesis 6–9: the Flood

These chapters describe the development of wickedness on the earth, and God's response to it. He instructed Noah to build an ark, and to take into it his family, pairs of every kind of animal and bird, and food. God then flooded the earth, destroying everything on it. Noah's family and animals escape in the ark, and, after the flood had subsided, repopulate the earth.[37]

Before the Flood, "the earth was corrupt before God, and filled with violence ... for all flesh had corrupted its way on the earth" (6:11–12). Here "all flesh" almost certainly includes animals, as elsewhere in the narrative (6:17, 19; 7:15–16, 21; 8:17; 9:11, 15–17).[38] Hence God's regret that he had made animals as well as human beings (6:7) and his destruction of them at the same time (6:17, 7:21–23).

The men described in 6:4 (Hebrew $n^e p \hat{\imath} l \hat{\imath} m$; Greek *gigantes*, "giants") appear again in Numbers 13:33. However, this need not mean that some of them survived the Flood: the later $n^e p \hat{\imath} l \hat{\imath} m$ could have been born after the Flood.

---

[36] Compare the discrepancy of two years between 5:32, 7:6, and 11:10 which may also be due to the use of round numbers.

[37] On the internal consistency of the narrative, see Kidner, *Genesis*, pp. 97–100.

[38] Cf. Wenham, *Genesis 1–15*, p. 171; Hamilton, *Genesis 1–17*, p. 279.

Noah took on to the ark pairs of every kind of land animal and bird (6:19–20, 7:2–3, 8–9, 14–16), and (lit.) "all food which may be eaten" (6:21). The narrator refers to two kinds of bird: *'ōrēḇ* (8:7) and *yônâ* (8:8–12). The first term is a broad one (Lev. 11:15, Deut. 14:14). According to scholars, it embraces at least five species (raven, fan-tailed raven, hooded crow, rook, and jackdaw).[39] The second term embraces at least three (rock dove, wood pigeon or ring dove, and stock dove). The narrator could have used these terms to refer to a single species (like "crow" in English): otherwise he again had a broad conception of kind.

The ark was large. Its dimensions were $300 \times 50 \times 30$ cubits (6:15) — about $150 \times 25 \times 15$ metres or $450 \times 75 \times 45$ feet.[40] It was therefore about the same size as the hull of a modern North Sea Ferry (e.g. Norstar, $173 \times 25 \times 17$ metres).

The narrator gives precise dates, as if Noah kept a log. These are, in years of Noah's life (cf. 7:6):[41]

17.2.600	Flood began (7:11)
	Waters rose, then receded
17.7.600	Ark grounded (8:4)
1.10.600	Mountain tops seen (8:5)
	Birds sent out (8:6–12)
1.1.601	Waters dried up (8:13)
27.2.601	Earth dry (8:14)

If the 40 days of rain and flood (7:12, 17) constitute part of the 150 days of the waters "prevailing" (7:24),[42] the five months between the first two dates span 150 days, plus the interval between the waters ceasing to prevail (8:3) and the ark grounding (8:4). If this interval was between 0 and 5 days, the months were between 30 and 31 days.

---

[39] Post, "Dove", "Raven"; Cansdale, *Animals of Bible Lands*, pp. 169–173, 181–184.
[40] Based on 1 cubit ≈ 0.5 metre or 1.5 feet.
[41] Heb. version. Gk. version has 27.2.600, 27.7.600, 1.11.600, 1.1.601, 27.2.601.
[42] Kidner, *Genesis*, p. 98–99.

The Flood was severe. It lasted about a year (see above). At its height, the waters covered "all the high mountains under all the heavens" (7:19–20) and extended over "the surface of all the earth" (8:9). I discuss this further below.

The author does not say what happened to the Garden of Eden (3:24) in the Flood. In the New Testament John is shown the tree of life in heaven (Rev. 22:1–2). Most commentators take this to mean that the garden in Genesis is symbolic, but it could imply that God took the garden up into heaven before the Flood, as he did Enoch (Gen. 5:24).

After the Flood, God instructed Noah and his sons to repopulate the earth (9:1, 7). He told them that they could now eat meat as long as they did not eat the blood (9:2–4), and imposed the death penalty on humans and animals that take human life (9:5–6). These rules were evidently designed to contain the violence that had developed before the Flood (6:11–12).

Finally, God covenanted not to flood the earth again (9:8–11), and made the rainbow a sign of this (9:12–17). The wording of 9:13 is ambiguous: it can be translated "I have set my bow", or "I set my bow", or even "I will set my bow".[43] The first implies that there were rainbows before the Flood, the second and third that there were not.

Extent of the Flood

Commentators are divided over the extent of the Flood. Most argue either that flooding was confined to the world known to Noah, or that it extended over the entire globe.[44] This question has both Biblical and scientific aspects. Here I shall concentrate on the former, leaving the latter to Chapter 5. I shall set out the Biblical arguments in the form of a debate, with L advocating a local flood and G a global one.

Language used

> **G:** The language used in the narrative ("all flesh", "all the earth", "under all the heavens") indicates a global flood.

---

[43] Driver, *Genesis*, p. 98.
[44] See, e.g., Ramm, *The Christian View of Science and Scripture,* Chap. 6, Sect. 3; Whitcomb and Morris, *The Genesis Flood*; Young, *The Biblical Flood.* For other references see Chapter 5.

L: In many places in the Bible, phrases like those used in the narrative refer to the world as people conceived it at the time, not as we know it today (e.g. "all the earth" in Gen. 41:57; "all flesh" in Ezek. 20:48; "all the world" in Luke 2:1; "every nation under heaven" in Acts 2:5; "the whole world" in Rom. 1:8; "every creature under heaven" in Col. 1:23).

G: The terminology is as global as it could be. In Genesis 1 "the earth" and "the heavens" have a wider meaning than its first readers would have appreciated.

God's regret

G: The behaviour of human beings and animals was such that God regretted that he had made them (6:6–7).

L: God could have regretted making human beings and animals because of the bad behaviour of those living in one area.

Nature of flood

G: The narrative states that (lit.) "all the springs of the great deep were ruptured, and the windows of the heavens were opened" (7:11). This implies a catastrophe of very major proportions. Peter wrote: "the then world perished, being flooded with water" (2 Pet. 3:6).

L: The flood had little lasting effect on rivers (cf. 2:10–14). Noah correctly anticipated that a dove would find olive trees growing after the waters had subsided (8:8–11).

Depth of water

G: The narrative states that, when the waters began to recede, the ark came to rest "on the mountains of Ararat (*^{a}rārāṭ*)" (8:3–4). Scholars identify Ararat as the region around or to the south of modern Mount Ararat (Fig. 4.1).[45] Mount Ararat is very high (5,200 metres or 17,000 feet). Thus if "all the high mountains" were covered (7:19–20), the greater part of the globe would necessarily have been covered.

L: There is some indication that the ancient Hebrews distinguished between the mountains on the horizon of their world, which they regarded as supporting the sky, and those rising within it (commentators take "the pillars of the heavens" in Job 26:11 as a reference to the

---

[45] Bryce, *Transcaucasia and Ararat*, Chap. 6; Cassuto, *A Commentary on the Book of Genesis*, Vol. 2; Wenham, *Genesis 1–15*, pp. 184–185. See also Rohl, *A Test of Time*, Vol. 2, Chaps. 2 and 4.

former).[46] If the ancient Hebrews did make this distinction, the flood could have been confined to a region surrounded by high mountains, including the mountains of Ararat. It would then have covered "all the high hills/mountains (*hārîm*)" within the region, but not the higher mountains around it. This would explain why the narrator states that, some 2½ months after the ark came to rest on the mountains of Ararat, "the tops of the hills/mountains were seen" (8:4–5).

Support for this interpretation is provided by the description of the Flood given by the Jewish philosopher Philo of Alexandria, writing in the 1st century A.D. Philo visualized the Flood as covering all the mountains within the world as he knew it, but not those on the edge of it:[47]

> ... the flood was not a trifling outpouring of water but a limitless and immense one, which almost flowed out beyond the Pillars of Hercules and the Great Sea. Therefore the whole earth and the mountainous regions were flooded.

The Pillars of Hercules are the rocks on either side of the Strait of Gibraltar.

G: In Job 26:11 the phrase "the pillars of the heavens" could be poetic. Verse 7a reads: "he stretches out the north over emptiness". (Compare also "pillars of the earth" in 9:6 and 26:7b: "he hangs the earth on nothing".)

Credibility

L: It is difficult to imagine Noah collecting animals from all over the globe, keeping them alive for 12 months, and returning them to suitable habitats after the flood. It is also difficult to believe that the ark drifted for 12 months over the globe, and finished up in the same region it started from.

G: God could have helped in the collection, care, and dispersal of the animals, and controlled the drifting of the ark. There is an indication of this in the narrative, which describes the animals as coming to Noah (6:20, 7:8–9, 15), God shutting the door of the ark (7:16), and acting to secure Noah's survival (8:1).

L: Noah would have needed God's help if the Flood had been local.

---

[46] See Whitehouse, "Cosmogony"; Hooke, *In the Beginning*, p. 20.
[47] *Questions and Answers on Genesis* 2:28 (Loeb edn.).

End of the Flood

L: The narrator says that God used a wind to make the waters recede (8:1). A wind could only do this if the Flood was local.

G: The "wind" (*rûaḥ*) could have been the Spirit of God (cf. 1:2). The word *rûaḥ* means "wind" or "spirit".

God's promise afterwards

G: After the Flood, God promised Noah that he would not flood the earth again (9:11). Since there have been many local floods since then, the reference must be to a global flood.

L: God's promise was to Noah and his descendants — he would never flood the whole of their world again. Their world has since expanded, and is now global.

Peter's description

G: Peter described the Flood in global terms: "God did not spare the ancient world, ... bringing the flood on the world of the ungodly" (2 Pet. 2:5); "the then world perished, being flooded with water" (2 Pet. 3:6); "a few, that is eight souls, were saved" (1 Pet. 3:20).

L: Peter's expressions "the ancient world" and "the then world" refer to Noah's world. Peter uses "world" (*kosmos*) not "earth" (*gē*, 2 Pet. 3:5, 13).

Other views

Some commentators have suggested that '*ereṣ* in the narrative means "land". This would make the flood a very local one, confining it to one area of the then-known earth. This would explain why Noah's descendants after the Flood feared being scattered by enemies (11:1–4, see below). However, the language of 7:19 ("under all the heavens") does not support a very local flood, and the fear of being scattered may reflect disbelief that the Flood destroyed other races. Elsewhere in Genesis, if '*ereṣ* refers to a land the land is specified (e.g. 10:31); otherwise the word has a wider meaning (e.g. 10:32).

The debate between L and G suggests a fourth possibility. Genesis describes the flooding of the world known to Noah — the region where he lived, up to the slopes of the surrounding mountains. At the same time, God flooded populated regions in other parts of the globe, and preserved sufficient fauna to repopulate them afterwards. The flooding was accordingly widespread, but did not cover the globe entirely.

Genesis 10 and 11: Noah to Abraham

These chapters describe the repopulation of the earth from Noah's sons, Shem, Ham, and Japheth. In 11:10–26 the line of descent from Shem to Terah and Abraham is given in similar detail to that from Adam to Noah and Shem in Genesis 5. There are again differences between the oldest texts, and the Greek version has an extra person in the line (Cainan, between Arphaxad and Shelah, 11:12).[48] Luke includes Cainan in his genealogy of Jesus (Luke 3:36).

Most scholars take Cainan to be an addition, to give the genealogy the same number of names as in Genesis 5 (ten), and make the two lists symmetrical (compare the $14 + 14 + 14$ structure of Mat. 1:1–17). However, for the translators to have added a name to the text, without a strong tradition to support it, would have been unlawful (Deut. 4:2, 12:32). Equally, omitting a name would have been unlawful. The addition/ omission of Cainan could be an indication that ancient scholars had grounds for believing that the genealogy is selective.

Most modern commentators identify the nations in Genesis 10 as occupying the area shown in Figure 4.1.[49] Many names are difficult to identify with certainty.

Genesis 10:25 contains the statement "the earth was divided". Some commentators take this to describe a second global catastrophe,[50] but most take it to refer to a division of population ('eres as in 11:1) or to the construction of a network of irrigation canals ('eres as in 11:2, pālaḡ as in Job 38:25).[51] The statement is made to explain the name Peleḡ.

---

[48] Skinner, *Genesis*, p. 233.
[49] See, e.g., Wenham, *Genesis 1–15*, pp. 216–232, 242–244.
[50] E.g., Norman and Setterfield, "The Atomic Constants, Light, and Time", Supplement.
[51] Kidner, *Genesis*, p. 109, etc. So Morris, *Biblical Creationism*, p. 47.

Genesis 11:1–9 describes the tower of Babel and confusion of languages. Its position in the narrative suggests that this episode took place after the dispersion of Genesis 10. However, the narrative makes better sense if the episode is taken as an explanation of the dispersion (cf. 10:5, 20, 31). On this reading, 11:1–4 describes the situation before the dispersal. Noah's descendants ("all the *'eres*") had one language (v. 1), and settled in Mesopotamia ("as they journeyed in the east [i.e. east of Canaan, as in 2:8], they found a plain in the land of Shinar, and dwelt there", v. 2). There they said, "Come, let us build ourselves a city, and a tower with its top in the heavens, and let us make a name for ourselves, lest we be scattered over the face of all the earth" (v. 4). God responded by confusing their language and scattering them (vv. 5–9).

Genesis 12–50 describes the history of Abraham, Isaac, Jacob, and Jacob's twelve sons.

Chronology

If the genealogies in Genesis 5 and 11:10–26 are complete they allow dates to be assigned to the Creation and the Flood, based on a date for the birth of Abraham. The latter can be obtained from Biblical and other data. The results are set out in Table 4.3. I have rounded the figures to the nearest ten years.

Table 4.3   Dates of Creation and the Flood if the genealogies in Genesis 5 and 11:10-26 are complete.[a]

	Heb.	*Sam.*	*Gk.*
Creation	4110 B.C.	4200 B.C.	5260[b]B.C.
Flood	2460 B.C.	2890 B.C.	3020 B.C.

[a] Based on the calculations of Driver, *Genesis*, pp. xxvi–xxviii, and a date of 971 B.C. for the beginning of the reign of Solomon. These give 1447 B.C. for the Exodus. Scholars are divided over whether this date is correct (Kitchen, *Ancient Orient and Old Testament*, Chap. 3; Rohl, *A Test of Time*, Vol. 1).
[b] Or 20 years earlier (Table 4.2. note c).

5 Evidence for the Flood

As discussed in the previous chapter, the Bible describes a major flood early in human history. The question is, is there any evidence for this flood? On this opinion varies.[1]

5.1 Preliminary considerations

As we saw in the previous chapter, the flood could have covered

(1) one land;

(2) the world known to Noah;

(3) this and other occupied areas of the globe;

(4) the entire globe.

The land in (1), and Noah's world in (2) and (3), must border the "mountains of Ararat", on the Turkish-Iranian plateau (Fig. 4.1). (1) is less well supported by the text than (2) and (4), and (3) is speculative.

Date

Radiocarbon dating

Radiocarbon dating is the main method by which archaeologists date human artefacts.[2] This gives the date at which organic matter died. The method requires a value for the proportion of radioactive carbon (carbon-14) in the atmosphere at the time. Early workers set this equal to the present-day value. Modern workers calibrate the method using wood

---

[1] Compare, e.g., Whitcomb and Morris, *The Genesis Flood*, and Young, *Creation and the Flood*. For a survey of views, see Young, *The Biblical Flood*.

[2] Aitken, *Science-based Dating in Archaeology*.

Table 5.1   Comparison of uncalibrated and calibrated radiocarbon dates (approx.).

Uncalibrated[a]	Calibrated[b]	Difference (years)
1000 B.C.	1200 B.C.	200
2000 B.C.	2500 B.C.	500
3000 B.C.	3700 B.C.	700
4000 B.C.	4800 B.C.	800
5000 B.C.	5900 B.C.	900
6000 B.C.	6900 B.C.	900
7000 B.C.	(8000 B.C.)	(1,000)[c]
8000 B.C.	(9000 B.C.)	(1,000)[c]
9000 B.C.	(10,000 B.C.)	(1,000)[c]
10,000 B.C.	(11,000 B.C.)	(1,000)[c]
11,000 B.C.	(12,000 B.C.)	(1,000)[c]

[a]Conventional (based on a half-life of 5568 years).
[b]From Aitken, *Science-based Dating in Archaeology*, Fig. 4.6 (p. 99).
[c]Tentative values, from Aitken, Table 2.3 (p. 12). Cf. Hajdas, Ivy-Ochs, and Bonani, "Problems in the Extension of the Radiocarbon Calibration Curve".

dated by matching and counting tree rings (dendrochronology) or material dated by counting varves (annual deposits of sediments in lakes).

The choice between these procedures is difficult. The older method reproduces Egyptian chronology based on historical data (king lists etc.),[3] whereas the modern method gives earlier dates, as shown in Table 5.1.[4] The earlier dates imply that Egyptian king lists are incomplete, a

[3] Aitken, *Science-based Dating*, Fig. 3.2 (p. 58).
[4] Aitken, *Science-based Dating*, pp. 98–99. Varve counting initially gave later dates, but now gives earlier ones (*ibid.*, pp. 35–36).

conclusion historians resist.[5] (This is similar to the question of whether the genealogies in Genesis 5 and 11 are complete.) In this chapter I shall quote both dates (calibrated/uncalibrated), with the author's in bold type. I shall quote dates based on historical data similarly (calibrated/historical).

Note that chronologists base uncalibrated radiocarbon dates on a conventional value for the half-life of carbon-14 (5568 years).[6] A more accurate value (5730 years) gives 3% earlier dates. The correction amounts to 150 years around 3000 B.C. and 300 years around 8000 B.C. Chronologists include this correction in the calibration. Note also that dates "before present" (B.P.) are reckoned from 1950 (i.e. 0 B.P. = 1950 A.D.).

Date of Flood

If the genealogy in Genesis 11:10–26 is complete, the date of the Flood is 2460, 2890, or 3020 B.C., depending on the version (Table 4.3). If the genealogy is incomplete, the Flood was earlier than this.

Now there is no evidence of a total flood of Egypt at any of these dates. The history of Egypt is unbroken from the beginning of the Naqada period (about **4000**/3300 B.C.) onwards.[7] The Nile overflowed annually, in some years more than in others, but the population was never wiped out. This means either that the Flood did not greatly affect Egypt and was confined to one land [(1) above], or that it occurred before the genealogical date, the geneaology in Genesis 11:10–26 being incomplete. In either case, Moses would have been aware of the situation, having been brought up in Egypt.

How much earlier the Flood could have been is constrained by Genesis 4. This describes how people lived before the Flood. They kept animals, cultivated crops, and worked metals (vv. 2b, 20–22). The Flood must have come after these activities began. I discuss this further below.

---

[5] See Rohl, *A Test of Time*, Vol. 1, App. C.
[6] Aitken, *Science-based Dating*, p. 93.
[7] Quirke and Spencer (eds.), *The British Museum Book of Ancient Egypt*.

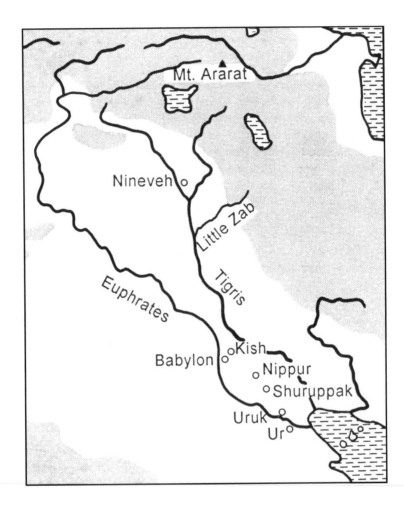

Figure 5.1 Sites in Mesopotamia referred to in the text. Most authorities identify Mount Niṣir as a mountain near the Little Zab. (After Parrot, *The Flood and Noah's Ark*, Fig. I, p. 33.)

Mesopotamian flood stories

Archaeologists have discovered in Mesopotamia several stories of a major flood, in which the hero escapes in a boat:[8]

* the story of King Ziusudra (fragmentary);
* the Epic of Atrahasis (fragmentary);
* the story of Utnapishtim in the Epic of Gilgamesh.

These are sufficiently similar for scholars to regard them as different versions of the same tale.

The first is the oldest. It is on a fragment of tablet found at Nippur (Fig. 5.1). This is in Sumerian, and dates from the late 3rd/early 2nd millennium B.C. There is also a reference to a flood in a Sumerian king list and other texts.[9] Scholars date Ziusudra, a king of Shuruppak, around 3550/2850 B.C.[10] Archaeologists have discovered deposits of water-borne clay at Shuruppak, Kish, and Uruk dating from about this time (they have also discovered deposits in the region dated at other times).[11]

The most complete version of the story is the third. This is on Tablet XI of the Epic of Gilgamesh. This was found at Nineveh, and is dated about 650 B.C. The text is in Akkadian. The story is very similar to Genesis in many ways (Box 5.1), but differs from it, not only in being polytheistic, but in the details of the flood. Utnapishtim lives at Shuruppak and his boat grounds on Mount Niṣir. The flood waters take only seven days to rise, and seven days or so to fall (lines 127–155). The waters also take only seven days to rise in the Sumerian version (lines 203–204). Noah's flood lasted over a year.

---

[8] Pritchard (ed.), *Ancient Near Eastern Texts*, pp. 42–44, 93–97, 104–106; Parrot, *The Flood and Noah's Ark*, pp. 22–37.

[9] Pritchard (ed.), *Ancient Near Eastern Texts*, pp. 265–266; Parrot, *The Flood and Noah's Ark*, pp. 41–42; Kramer, "Reflections on the Mesopotamian Flood: The Cuneiform Data New and Old".

[10] Mallowan, "Noah's Flood Reconsidered"; Kramer, "Reflections on the Mesopotamian Flood". Rohl (*A Test of Time*, Vol. 2, Chap. 5) estimates the date of the flood as 3800/3100 B.C.

[11] Parrot, *The Flood and Noah's Ark*, pp. 45–53; Mallowan, "Noah's Flood Reconsidered". Rohl (*A Test of Time*, Vol. 2, Chap. 5) attributes the thick deposit at Ur to the epic flood, and redates this deposit accordingly.

Box 5.1

Flood story in the Epic of Gilgamesh (Tablet XI)[a]

Gilgamesh asks his ancestor, Utnapishtim, how he had gained eternal life. Utnapishtim tells him that, when he was living in the city of Shuruppak, the gods, led by Enlil, determined to flood it.[b] The sea-god Ea warned him about this, and told him to build a ship. He did this, and took on to it silver and gold, his family and relations, domestic and wild animals, and craftsmen. The deluge came, and was so severe that the gods were frightened by it. On the seventh day, the storm subsided, and the boat came to rest on Mount Niṣir. Seven days later, Utnapishtim sent out a dove, which returned; then a swallow, which also returned; and finally a raven, which did not come back. He then disembarked, and offered a sacrifice to the gods, who gathered round it "like flies". Enlil was angry, but Ea reasoned with him, and Enlil made Utnapishtim and his wife like gods.

[a]Pritchard (ed.), *Ancient Near Eastern Texts*, pp. 93–95; Parrot, *The Flood and Noah's Ark,* pp. 25–31.

[b]In the Epic of Atrahasis, the reason given for this is that humans were making too much noise, and keeping the gods from sleep.

Despite these differences, most scholars assume that Genesis describes the same flood as the epics, and that its author derived his story from the Mesopotamian one by removing its polytheism. The first assumption is supported by the dates (epic 3550/2850 B.C.; Genesis, genealogical date 3020, 2890, or 2460 B.C.), but the second is very unlikely, partly for the reasons I gave in Chapter 3, and partly because it implies that the author of Genesis made up the details of the flood.

A more plausible explanation of the similarity between Genesis and the epics is that the author of the story in the epics rewrote the history of *Noah's* escape in Sumer, replacing Noah's god by his own gods, and symbolizing the length of the flood (the ancients regarded seven as a sacred number).[12] This is not entirely satisfactory, as it makes Noah's flood very local.

An alternative explanation is that the flood in the epics took place

[12] Cf. Mallowan, "Noah's Flood Reconsidered", pp. 63–64.

after Noah's, and that either (1) the author of the story in the epics incorporated elements of what he knew about the earlier flood in writing about the later one, or (2) the survivor of the later flood was inspired by Noah in preparing for a flood (Mesopotamia is prone to flooding) and in sending out birds. This means that Noah's flood took place before the genealogical date.

Noah's world

Genesis gives the impression that the world known to Noah was around Eden (2:8–14, 3:23–24). There is no reference to the dispersal of humans, or to Mesopotamia or Egypt, until after the Flood (10–11). Cain settled east of Eden (4:16), but Noah knew enough about his descendants to record their history (4:17–24). These considerations, and those on the location of Eden in the previous chapter, place Noah's world on the Turkish-Iranian plateau (Chap. 4, Fig. 4.1), at a time when its inhabitants did not know about other parts of the Middle East or wider world.

This dates Noah's world before about 9000/8000 B.C. After this date, archaeologists have evidence of trade between different settlements in the Middle East, and of transmission of culture.[13] Trade was in obsidian, a dark volcanic rock found on the Turkish-Iranian plateau.

Moreover, the culture was of the kind described in Genesis 4. Archaeologists have found evidence of agriculture dating from about 9000/**8000** B.C.,[14] and of metal-working from about 8500/**7500** B.C. (Fig. 5.2).[15] Genesis gives the impression that these activities originated in Noah's world, and were disseminated by his descendants after the Flood (cf. 4:20–22). The wild forms of the cereals early farmers cultivated (wheat and barley) grow on the Turkish-Iranian plateau.[16]

[13] Mellaart, *The Neolithic of the Near East*, p. 9.

[14] Zohary and Hopf, *Domestication of Plants in the Old World*.

[15] Mellaart, *The Neolithic of the Near East*, pp. 52–54, 283–284. Early metalworkers used naturally occurring metals (native copper, meteoritic iron) and worked them by hammering and grinding; smelting of ores came later. Genesis 4:22 describes Tubal-Cain as a "sharpener" (Heb.) or "hammerer" (Gk.) of copper and iron.

[16] Zohary and Hopf, *Domestication of Plants in the Old World*; Diamond, "Location, Location, Location: The First Farmers", Heun and others, "Site of Einkorn Wheat Domestication Identified by DNA Fingerprinting". Cf. Barraclough and Parker (eds.), *The Times Atlas of World History*, pp. 40–41.

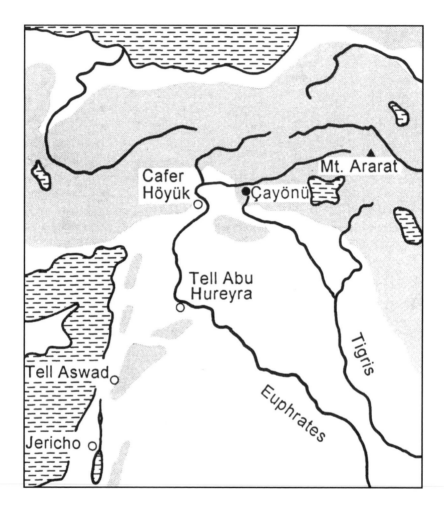

Figure 5.2 Map showing sites where archaeologists have found evidence of agriculture and metal-working at an early date (9000/8000 to 8500/7500 B.C.). O, agriculture; ●, both. (From refs. 14–16.)

Noah's world is unlikely to have been very much earlier than 9000/
8000 B.C. because of the last Ice Age, which ended at about this date.
According to one study, at the peak of the Ice Age (*ca.* 17,000 B.C.
uncalibrated), the snow-line on the Turkish-Iranian plateau was 1,000–
1,200 metres lower than it is now, and temperatures in July were 6–8° C
below their present values.[17]

If my impressions of Genesis are incorrect, Noah's world could have
been wider and later than I have suggested.

Conclusions

The possibilities are:

(1) a flood on the Turkish-Iranian plateau towards the end of the last
Ice Age (9000/8000 B.C.);

(2) a flood of a wider area of the Middle East between this date and
the beginning of the Naqada period in Egypt (4000/3300 B.C.);

(3) a widespread flood between the latter part of the last Ice Age and
the Naqada period in Egypt;

(4) a global flood between these dates.

A less satisfactory possibility is that the Flood took place around the
genealogical date, and was confined to Mesopotamia. This requires *'ereṣ*
in Genesis 6–9 to be taken as "land", and the stories in Genesis 10–11 to
apply to Noah's descendants within a wider world (cf. Rohl, *A Test of
Time*, Vol. 2).

5.2 Evidence for a global flood

Flood stories

There are stories of a major flood, early in human history, from many
parts of the globe (Fig. 5.3).[18] These resemble the Genesis story in

---

[17] See Brinkmann, *Geology of Turkey*, pp. 79–81. Cf. Nützel, "The Climate Changes of
Mesopotamia and Bordering Areas: 14000 to 2000 B.C."; Brice (ed.), *The Environmental History
of the Near and Middle East since the Last Ice Age*.

[18] See, e.g., Frazer, *Folk-lore in the Old Testament*, Vol. 1. For further references, see Lang,
"Non-Semitic Deluge Stories and the Book of Genesis: A Bibliographic and Critical Survey".

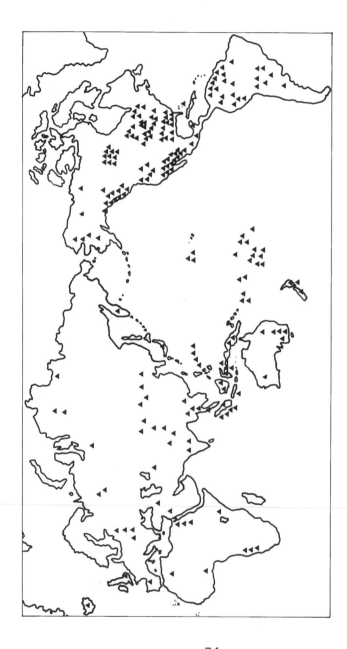

Figure 5.3 Places where flood stories have been found. (After Lang, "Non-Semitic Deluge Stories", Map 1.)

describing a flood of world-wide proportions, the escape of a small number of survivors, and the repopulation of the world from them. Beyond this the details differ. For example, in a Hindu story, there is one survivor, who is helped to escape by a fish, and is provided with a partner afterwards.

This evidence is difficult to interpret. On the one hand, many of these stories could have come from the survivors of a global flood, whose descendants took the story to different parts of the globe, where it subsequently became corrupted. On the other hand, many of the stories could have arisen out of floods in the localities concerned. Their resemblance to Genesis would then be either coincidental, or the result of assimilation, after travellers or missionaries had brought the Genesis story to a locality. Major floods are certainly a common occurrence in many parts of the globe, and missionary influence is widespread.[19] Even so the multiplicity of similar stories is striking.[20]

Geological evidence

Some Biblical Christian geologists take the view that a global flood is unlikely to leave very much of a mark on the earth's crust.[21] They argue that, when there is a flood, most of the water-borne clay that is deposited is subsequently eroded away, leaving only pockets that become consolidated. That a wide area has been affected is therefore difficult to prove, as there will be geographical breaks between deposits, and little to distinguish the latter from deposits produced by more localized flooding.

Donald Boardman, however, takes the opposite view.[22] He argues that it should be possible to identify strata produced by a global flood. He also contends that the draining of global quantities of floodwater should leave distinctive marks of erosion. In the absence of such evidence he concludes that the Flood could not have been global.

---

[19] Vitaliano, *Legends of the Earth*, Chap. 7.
[20] Custance, "Flood Traditions of the World".
[21] E.g. Young, *Creation and the Flood*, pp. 172–174.
[22] Boardman, "Did Noah's Flood Cover the Entire World? — No".

As we saw in Chapter 2, some Biblical Christian scientists disagree with this conclusion (Sect. 2.6). They believe that the Flood was sufficiently catastrophic that most of the strata in the earth's crust were laid in this event and its aftermath. These strata thereby constitute proof of a global flood. However, most professional geologists reject this analysis, including Biblical Christian ones (Sect. 2.6). They believe that many strata were laid catastrophically, but not in a single event.

One geologist has claimed that there is evidence that debris from a comet struck the earth around **7600/6600** B.C. and caused a global flood.[23] His main geological evidence is the occurrence of tektites (glassy rocks) dated about 7600/6600 B.C. in several parts of the globe. Other geologists, however, date these tektites much earlier and reject the idea that an impact of debris would cause a global flood.[24]

Archaeological evidence

A Biblical Christian anthropologist and archaeologist, Victor Pearce, claims that there is archaeological evidence for a global flood.[25] He argues that a global flood would not be expected to leave deposits of water-borne clay everywhere, because of erosion, but that it would be expected to leave a hiatus in human and animal remains everywhere. He says that, in the Old World, there is such a hiatus. This is between strata containing Copper-Stone Age remains, which date to about 6000/**5000** B.C., and strata containing Bronze Age ones, which date from about 5000/4000 B.C., a gap of about 1,000 years. This break in culture is marked by a thick deposit of water-borne clay at, for example, Ur and Nineveh, dated about **5000/4000** B.C.[26]

Pearce says that there is also a hiatus in the New World commencing at about this date. This is between deposits containing the remains of

---

[23] Kristan-Tollmann and Tollmann, "The Youngest Big Impact on Earth Deduced from Geological and Historical Evidence".

[24] Deutsch and others, "The Impact-Flood Connection: Does it Exist?"; cf. Kristan-Tollmann and Tollmann, "Reply to a Reply — But the Flood Really Happened!"

[25] Pearce, *Who Was Adam?*, Chap. 9; *Evidence for Truth*, Vol. 1, Chaps. 12–15.

[26] This date should coincide with that for the beginning of the hiatus. The agreement is thus only approximate.

Old World animals that are no longer in the New World, and deposits containing the remains of New World animals only. The strata between these contain no animals, and span 1,000–3,000 years.

Pearce's work merits careful evaluation by those competent to do this, especially in relation to the New World. Biblical Christian geologist Davis Young knows of no break in human populations in North America or Australia at the date Pearce suggests.[27] Geneticists do trace modern humans to a small number of individuals, but much earlier, albeit using estimated mutation rates (Chap. 2, Sect. 2.5). Genetic studies of human remains may eventually clarify the history of modern humans.

Pearce also refers to mammoths. Remains of large numbers of these have been found in various places — in Siberia frozen in ice. However, radiometric dating indicates that the animals died at various times, between 40,000 and 10,000 years ago (uncalibrated).[28]

Pearce notes that, in Europe and the Middle East, there is also a hiatus between Upper Old Stone Age strata and Middle Stone Age ones. This starts about 12,000/**11,000** B.C. and finishes about 10,000/**9000** B.C. He says that this could be due to a flood, but not to Noah's, because 12,000/**11,000** B.C. is too early for metal-working (cf. Sect. 5.1).

5.3 Evidence for a flood of Noah's world

As I discussed in Section 5.1, Noah's world was probably on the Turkish-Iranian plateau towards the end of the last Ice Age (9000/8000 B.C.). There is no evidence of a flood on the plateau at this time, but it is an area that has been relatively little studied.[29] Access to it is currently very difficult.

If Noah's world was wider and later than I suggested in Section 5.1, Pearce's evidence for a flood of the Old World around 5000/4000 B.C. (Sect. 5.2) would apply. Note that a local flood can last for a year if the

---

[27] Young, *The Biblical Flood*, pp. 233–235.
[28] Young, *The Biblical Flood*, pp. 228–230.
[29] Cf. Mellaart, *The Neolithic of the Near East*.

floodwaters build up a barrier of sediment. Such a flood occurred in the Sinai Desert in 1971.[30] This lasted 21 months until further flooding broke the dam.

Oceanographers William Ryan and Walter Pitman have suggested that the stories of a major flood in the Middle East have their origin in a rapid expansion of the Black Sea.[31] They have assembled evidence that, when the level of the Mediterranean rose after the last Ice Age, its waters breached the Bosporus and poured into the Black Sea. At the time this was a freshwater lake, below the level of the Mediterranean. There was consequently a rapid flooding of a wide area around the lake. However, the flooding was permanent; the waters did not recede as in the Genesis flood.

5.4 Evidence for a widespread flood

If Noah's world was on the Turkish-Iranian plateau towards the end of the last Ice Age, there could have been floods in other parts of the world at about the same time. Geologists have evidence of major floods during this period, arising from the build-up of melt-waters against barriers, and from the breaking of barriers.[32] Pearce's hiatus between Upper Old Stone Age and Middle Stone Age culture, dated 12,000/11,000 to 10,000/9000 B.C. (Sect. 5.2), falls in this period. This could indicate an early date for the Flood, a slow recovery of human populations, and a long delay before Noah's descendants dispersed their knowledge of agriculture and metal-work (cf. Sect. 5.1).

If Noah's world was wider and later than I have supposed, Pearce's evidence for a global flood around 5000/4000 B.C. could be evidence of a widespread flood at this date.

The flood stories from many parts of the world (Sect. 5.2) could also be evidence of a widespread flood.

---

[30] Schick and Lekach, "A High Magnitude Flood in the Sinai Desert".
[31] Kerr, "Black Sea Deluge May Have Helped Spread Farming".
[32] See, e.g., Cornwall, *Ice Ages*; Ager, *The New Catastrophism*, pp.19–23.

Part II

Reconciliation of the Biblical Account of Origins to the Scientific One

6 God's role in creation if the scientific account is correct

In this part of the book I shall assume that the orthodox scientific account of origins (big bang and evolution) is correct, and consider how far the Biblical account can be reconciled to it without the Bible losing its authority. This does not mean that the scientific account *is* correct. I am just taking it to be correct for the purpose of determining how far the Bible can be reconciled to it.

To prepare the ground for this consideration, we must first address the question: if the scientific account is correct, what part did God play in it? The account makes no reference to God, and seems to leave little room for God. Indeed some authors use it to argue that there isn't a God.[1] How can God be said to have created the universe if science is right?

6.1 Natural processes

To answer this question, we must first consider the kinds of process that appear in the scientific account. There are essentially two:[2]

Determined processes

An example of a determined process is a shot in a game of snooker. What happens to the balls is determined by the way the white ball is struck, and the positions of the balls on the table. A good player can repeat a shot many times, and the balls always finish up in the same places. In scientific terms, the motion of the balls is determined by the laws of mechanics and

---

[1] Monod, *Chance and Necessity*; Dawkins, *The Blind Watchmaker* and other books; Atkins, *The Creation/Creation Revisited*.
[2] Cf. Nelson, *God's Control over the Universe*, Sects. 2 and 3.

the initial state of the system (the state the instant the white ball is struck). Given details of the mechanical properties of the balls and the table, a scientist could calculate from the laws of motion what will happen when there is a particular arrangement of balls on the table and the white ball is struck in a particular way.

Many natural processes are of this kind. The motion of the earth round the sun and of the moon round the earth are determined by the laws of mechanics and gravity. From these laws scientists can predict the positions of the earth and the moon at future times from a knowledge of their positions at past times.

Scientists now know that, for many determined systems, a very accurate knowledge is needed of the state of a system for future states to be predicted accurately.[3] This is because the effect of errors on the calculations increases over time. This is known from models of the weather. These give completely different forecasts after a period of time if slightly different input data are used. Under unstable weather conditions this period is only a few hours. This sensitivity places severe limitations on scientists' ability to predict the future states of physical systems (including repeated collisions of balls on a table, and the solar system on a long time scale). However, these limits are practical, not theoretical.[4]

Some scientists believe that complex natural systems are governed by laws relating to a system as a whole as well as to its parts (Chap. 2, Sects. 2.3 and 2.4). This is possible. However, the laws in question may actually arise from the disposition of the parts.[5] Soldiers marching to a pattern obey the laws of the pattern as well as the laws of marching.

Indeterminate processes

When a snooker player makes a shot, he knows that, if he strikes the ball in a particular way, the result will always be the same. For example, if he strikes the ball against the cushion at the edge of the table, he knows that,

---

[3] See, e.g., Gleick, *Chaos*; Ruelle, *Chance and Chaos*; Hall (ed.), *The New Scientist Guide to Chaos*.
[4] Nelson, *God's Control*, Sect. 3.1.1.
[5] Nelson, *God's Control*, Sect. 2.2.4.

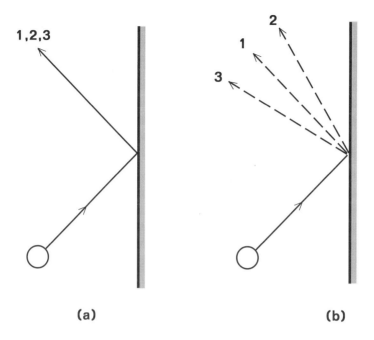

Figure 6.1   A snooker ball striking a cushion without any spin. The numbers refer to repetitions of the shot. In (a) the outcome is determined, in (b) indeterminate.

if he does not give the ball any spin, it will always rebound at the same angle (Fig. 6.1a). Imagine, however, that this was not the case — that when a ball strikes a cushion without any spin, it sometimes rebounds in one direction, sometimes in another, sometimes in another, in a completely random fashion (Fig. 6.1b). Under these circumstances the motion of the ball can no longer be predicted.

Although snooker balls do not behave like this, scientists believe that microscopic objects do. They have a theory (the quantum theory) that enables them to predict the probability that a microscopic particle will bounce off a barrier in a particular direction, and thus the number of particles that bounce off in this direction when a large number strike the barrier in succession. But they cannot calculate the direction in which any particular particle will come off.

Some scientists believe that this is because we do not know enough about microscopic objects. If a snooker table was in a wind-tunnel, the direction a ball bounced off a cushion would depend on the wind. Perhaps microscopic objects have influences upon them of which we are presently unaware. Other scientists, however, believe that indeterminacy is an intrinsic feature of microscopic systems.[6]

Scientists who take the second view frequently attribute the outcome of an individual microscopic event to "chance". For some this is simply another way of saying that the outcome of such an event cannot be predicted from its circumstances — it has no immediate cause. Others use the word "chance" to mean that an event has no ultimate cause,[1] but this goes beyond science (see below).

Microscopic processes are only indeterminate individually. When the same process takes place many times, the distribution of outcomes is fixed, and can be calculated from the quantum theory. For example, in a mineral containing uranium atoms, while it is impossible to predict when an individual atom will decay, it is possible to calculate the percentage of atoms that will decay over a period of time.

Since microscopic processes generally occur in nature in large numbers, their influence on the evolution of the universe is thus, for the most part, determined. Suppose, however, that radiation from a decaying uranium atom in a rock happens to strike a gene in an organism living nearby. Suppose further that the radiation happens to induce a mutation that is to the organism's advantage. This evolutionary event depends on the outcome of individual microscopic processes and is therefore indeterminate.

Randomness is an essential part of nature. For example, gases are

[6] Davies and Brown (eds.), *The Ghost in the Atom*.
[1] Monod, *Chance and Necessity*; Dawkins, *The Blind Watchmaker* and other books; Atkins, *The Creation/Creation Revisited*.

made up of microscopic particles moving randomly in all directions. This gives them the properties they have. If the particles all moved in the same direction, gases would have quite different properties. For example, if all the particles in the atmosphere moved from east to west, they would generate a continual high wind that would make human life impossible. Biologists believe that random mutations provide a means by which organisms can adapt to major changes in their environment.

According to modern science, then, the universe has evolved by a combination of determined and indeterminate processes. Evolution has taken the particular course that it has as a result of:

(1) the particular structure the universe had at the beginning of the big bang;

(2) the laws governing all the determined processes in the universe;

(3) the laws governing the distribution of outcomes of all the indeterminate processes; and

(4) the individual outcomes of indeterminate processes in key instances.

This conclusion is quite general, and is not tied to any particular mechanism of evolutionary change.

6.2 God's role

Our question is: if the scientific account of creation is correct, what part did God play in it? The answer is that he planned everything that happened, and brought it about.[7]

Firstly, God chose the laws of nature [items (2) and (3) above]. According to some cosmologists, even a slight change in these laws would have produced a universe that is quite different from our own. They speak as if the laws have to be finely tuned to produce a universe in which human beings can exist (the so-called "anthropic principle").[8] Other cosmologists have questioned this, arguing, for example, that there could

---

[7] Cf. Nelson, *God's Control*.

[8] Davies, *The Accidental Universe*; Barrow and Tipler, *The Anthropic Cosmological Principle*; Gribbin and Rees, *The Stuff of the Universe/Cosmic Coincidences*.

be an underlying law which fixes the relationship between the presently known ones,[9] or that the big bang model, in which most of the fine-tuning appears, is wrong (cf. Chap. 2, Sect. 2.1). What is certain is that, of all the possible laws or sets of laws that God could have chosen, only for some would the universe be hospitable to human beings, and only for one would it be exactly as it is.

Secondly, if the scientific account is correct, God chose the components of the speck of matter from which the universe exploded, and the arrangement of these components within the speck [item (1) above]. This arrangement determined the way in which the universe began to evolve, and the structures that developed within it. If all the processes in the universe were completely determined, the initial arrangement and the laws would fix the whole of its history, right down to the finest details. It would be like an embryo programmed by its DNA to develop into a particular organism.

Thirdly, if there are indeterminate processes in nature, God determined what the outcomes of these should be [items (3) and (4) above]. Scientists who say that such processes have no ultimate cause go beyond science.[10] Science is concerned only with immediate causes. God can as well determine the outcome of (to us) indeterminate events as he can, through his laws, determinate ones.[11]

God does not have to determine the outcome of such events individually. For any particular process, he can choose a random sequence of outcomes, consistent with a particular distribution [item (3) above]. Such sequences can be generated mathematically. On computers random numbers are produced by mathematical methods. Scientists use these numbers to simulate random processes in nature.

God can also choose sequences of outcomes to secure a coincidental event, of the kind described in the previous section. Thus, if, for a particular mutation to take place in a gene, radiation from a radioactive atom has to strike the gene, and the gene has to react in a particular way,

---

[9] Weinberg, *Dreams of a Final Theory*.
[10] See, e.g., MacKay, *Science, Chance, and Providence*, Chap. 2.
[11] Cf. Prigogine and Stengers, *Order out of Chaos*, pp. 271–272.

Table 6.1   Sets of random numbers between one and six.

Serial no.	1	2	3	4	5	6	7	8	9	10
Set A	1	6	2	1	4	5	3	5	4	5
Set B	3	5	2	2	1	4	5	1	3	**6**
Set C	3	4	3	6	1	3	2	4	2	4
Set D	4	2	3	5	2	1	3	5	3	4
Set E	1	6	4	1	6	1	5	2	4	3
Set F	4	6	1	3	3	1	6	4	1	2
Set G	6	4	1	4	2	5	1	5	6	3
Set H	6	4	5	5	3	2	1	4	1	**6**
Set I	2	2	1	3	3	2	6	5	5	1
Set J	5	3	6	2	5	6	4	6	2	2

then, to secure this mutation, God can match the random sequences that determine the decay of the atom with those that govern the reaction of the gene.

This can be illustrated by using the sets of random numbers in Table 6.1 to specify the results of throwing two dice. To obtain a double six after the tenth throw, one can use set B for one of the dice and set H for the other.

Finally, having planned the universe, God created it — he brought it into being. If the universe indeed began as a speck of highly concentrated matter, he made that speck of matter. Scientists who argue that the big bang arose from a chance fluctuation in nothing[12] confound the word nothing. A vacuum that can fluctuate and generate matter is not nothing.

---

[12] Tryon, "Is the Universe a Vacuum Fluctuation?"; Atkins, *The Creation/Creation Revisited*.

In conclusion, God is capable of creating the universe on the scientific picture, and of determining the entire course of its evolution, down to the finest detail. This includes the origin of life, the evolution of species, and the emergence of human beings. This is not to say that he did create the universe in this way, but he could have done.

This conclusion holds also for models of the universe on which it does not have a beginning (Chap. 2, Sect. 2.1). On these models the universe still has to be brought into being, as discussed in Chapter 9. It has accordingly still to be constructed in a particular manner to evolve into the universe as it now is.

Some scientists seek to avoid this conclusion by suggesting that there are an infinite number of universes (with a small u), either existing separately, or as different regions of an infinite Universe (capital U).[13] A random distribution of laws, starting conditions, and indeterminate outcomes among these universes would then generate the universe we inhabit without having to invoke divine choice. However, there is no evidence that there are other universes.[14] Even if there are, they still have to be brought into being, and randomness established between them.

Physicist Lee Smolin has suggested that new universes are formed inside black holes (collapsing stars) and that fine-tuning is a result of natural selection among universes formed in this way.[15] However, his universe-producing Universe still has to be brought into being, and given the capacity to generate a variety of universes on which natural selection can operate.

6.3 An analogy: Dawkins' insect

God's role in creation if the scientific account is correct is illustrated by an analogy from an unexpected quarter — Richard Dawkins' *The Blind Watchmaker*. In this book Dawkins describes a computer program he devised to illustrate biological evolution by random mutations and natural

---

[13] See Leslie, *Universes*; Layzer, *Cosmogenesis*; Deutsch, *The Fabric of Reality*.

[14] One interpretation of the quantum theory posits other worlds, but this is only a speculative idea, to which there are alternatives (note 6).

[15] Smolin, *The Life of the Cosmos*.

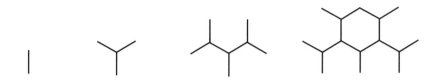

Figure 6.2   Patterns produced by successive branching.

selection.[16] This program draws a pattern on a screen according to a basic procedure and a set of rules. The basic procedure is to start with a line, put branches on it, put branches on the branches, and so on, as shown in Figure 6.2. The rules determine how many times the branching is repeated, how long the lines are, and the angles between them. The rules therefore resemble genes — they determine the form a pattern takes. A rule can remain the same from one pattern to another, or change incrementally (e.g. a line that is 5 units long in one pattern can be 4, 5, or 6 units long in the next).

Now the program begins by putting the simplest possible pattern on the screen (a dot). It then allows the variable quantities to change randomly by one unit up or down, to produce a series of new patterns. These changes represent mutations. The operator then surveys the new patterns, selects one to take forward, and eliminates the rest. This operation could be computerized, according to specific selection criteria, but this would make the program more complicated. The program then takes the selected pattern and produces a further series of patterns from this. The operator selects one of these, the program produces more patterns, and so on.

Dawkins found that his program produces complex patterns very quickly. He took this to support his contention that complex organisms have evolved by random mutations and natural selection and do not require anyone to have designed them.

However, Dawkins also found that some of the patterns are remarkably life-like (he calls them "biomorphs"). He was particularly delighted with

[16] Dawkins, *The Blind Watchmaker*, pp. 50–65.

Figure 6.3   Dawkins' insect.

one that looks very much like an insect (Fig. 6.3). When he first obtained this, he had not programmed his computer to record the sequence of changes that had produced it. He consequently had a great deal of difficulty obtaining an insect again. Eventually, however, he did obtain one, and this time he did record the sequence of changes so that he could reproduce it. In his own words, "now I can 'evolve' insects whenever I want".

This reveals the flaw in his conclusion that evolution does not involve a designer. While he was disinterested in the patterns he obtained, he could use any series of random changes and select from these. Once he wanted to produce a particular pattern, however, he had to choose his sequence of changes accordingly. In terms of his original program, he had to ensure that the random series of changes at each stage included the one he wanted to select. This does not make the series any less random in a mathematical sense (increases and decreases still occur in approximately equal proportions), but the *choice* of series ceases to be random. The choice becomes part of the design.

So it is with the universe. If it is true that all living organisms have evolved by random mutations and natural selection, they have done so according to a particular series of mutations. Other series would have produced different organisms. Like Dawkins with his insect, God chose the particular series of mutations that would generate the organisms he wanted, and made this part of his design.

Thus God could have created the universe in the way that science describes. This does not itself harmonize science and the Bible (e.g. it makes God wholly responsible for suffering), but it is a step in this direction.

7   Interpreting Genesis

To reconcile the Biblical account of origins to the scientific one, we must next consider the interpretation of Genesis 1–11. On this scholars, past and present, are divided. Josephus, for example, took Genesis 2–3 literally, presenting it as an explanation of nature (*Jewish Antiquities* 1:34–51, Loeb edn.). On the other hand, Philo interpreted it allegorically, with Adam symbolizing mind, Eve perception, the Serpent pleasure, and so on (*Allegorical Interpretation of Genesis 2–3*).

Let us start from the assumption that the narrative should be taken literally (cf. Chap. 4). This does not mean that every single word is taken literally. Some figurative language occurs in most writing. But it does mean that the *story-line* is taken literally. The question is, is this assumption reasonable?

To answer this we must consider the literary composition of Genesis 1–11, and the use of figurative language in the Bible.

7.1   Composition

Scholars are agreed that Genesis 1–11 is prose rather than poetry. Hebrew poetry is characterized by couplets in which the second line repeats the thought of the first (cf. Gen. 49:2–27). Genesis 1–11 does not have this structure.

However, some scholars have argued that parts of Genesis 1–11 do have a literary structure.[1] In Genesis 1, for example, they point out that:

(1) there is a repetition in the way in which events are described

---

[1] See Blocher, *In the Beginning*; Wenham, *Genesis 1–15*.

(typically "And God said, 'Let there be ...' And it was so. And God saw that it was good");

(2) there is a pattern in the number of times the phrase "And God said, 'Let there be'" is used:

day 1 once	day 4 once
day 2 once	day 5 once
day 3 twice	day 6 twice

(3) there is a correspondence between what is made on days 1–3 and 4–6:

day 1 light	day 4 luminaries
day 2 sea and sky	day 5 fish and birds
day 3 land and plants	day 6 animals and man

(4) there is a symmetrical structure to verses 14–18, with verse 18 repeating verse 14 and verse 17 repeating verse 15:

verse 14	verse 18
verse 15	verse 17
verse 16	

Scholars argue from this that the days in Genesis 1 are themselves part of the literary construction, and are not to be taken literally. However, this does not necessarily follow. The main elements of Genesis 1, including the six days and items (2) and (3), could have been determined by what happened, with the author employing literary devices like (1) and (4) to bring what happened out. Even so, the structure of Genesis 1 does raise the question of whether the author intended it to be semi-poetic, and to be interpreted accordingly. The same applies to other passages that have literary structure to them.

7.2 Use of figurative language in the Bible

Figurative language is used in the Bible for at least four purposes:

(1) to express truths that would be impossible to express literally;

(2) to express truths more vividly than they can be expressed literally;

(3) to express truths more simply than they can be expressed literally; and

(4) to express truths more obscurely than they can be expressed literally.

I shall discuss these in turn in relation to Genesis 1–11.

Expressing the inexpressible

The authors of the Bible had to write about many things that cannot be seen, and which cannot therefore be described literally. In particular, they had to write about God, Satan, heaven, and hell. To do this they had to use figurative language. So, for example, Jesus spoke of the Holy Spirit as "the finger of God" (compare Luke 11:20 with Mat. 12:28).

Genesis 1–11 contains figurative language used for this purpose (e.g., in 3:8 God is described as "walking in the garden"). However, this does not mean that the whole of Genesis 1–11 is written in this style. Figurative language is only needed to describe the spiritual aspects of creation and of the history of the world. If the author of Genesis used figurative language to describe the physical aspects, he must have had some other reason for doing so.

Enhancement

The authors of the Bible frequently use figurative language for the purposes of enhancement. For example, on one occasion, Jesus declared, "I am the light of the world. Whoever follows me shall never walk in darkness, but shall have the light of life" (John 8:12). This evokes a picture of walking in the country on a dark night. Without a light one can easily stumble or get lost (cf. John 11:9–10, 12:35–36, 1 John 2:9–11). Jesus could have said, "I can help people through life. Those who put their trust in me and follow my teaching will know how to live and avoid making mistakes." This still has force, but is not as graphic as what he did say.

In the story of Adam and Eve (2:4–3:24) there are a number of words and phrases that could come into this category. For example, the "tree of life" (2:9, 3:22) could symbolize God's provision for Adam of eternal life, and "the serpent" (3:1–5, 14–15) could symbolize the devil. However, these expressions could equally well be taken literally. There could have been a tree whose fruit conferred eternal life, if only miraculously (cf. Num. 21:8–9, etc.); and there could have been a creature with the faculty of speech and reason who became the devil (Chap. 4). Moreover, parts of the story seem very much as if they are intended to be taken literally (e.g. the geography of Eden, 2:10–14). The narrative could therefore be in an elevated style, but this is by no means certain.[2]

There is little evidence that the remainder of Genesis 1–11 is in such a style.

Simplification

Figurative language is often used in secular writing to make complicated ideas more intelligible to an ordinary reader. For example, an atom is often described as being like a tiny solar system, with a nucleus at the centre, and electrons orbiting round it like planets round the sun. This gives a reader some idea of what scientists believe an atom is like, even though, in certain respects, the picture is a gross over-simplification (e.g. electrons are not in well-defined orbits in the way that planets are).

The question is, does Genesis give a simplified account of origins, written to make what would otherwise have been unintelligible to early readers understandable to them? Were the stories in it devised, not to communicate the scientific truth about what happened, but the theological truth (e.g. that God, the God of Israel, created the universe)?

Now in part the answer to these questions must be "Yes". The ancient Hebrews did not have the scientific knowledge we have today. If Genesis had been written in modern scientific terms, they would not have been able to understand it. That God should inspire the author to describe creation in a way the ancient Hebrews could understand is entirely reasonable.

---

[2] This conclusion is not affected by the way terms in Genesis 2-3 are used elsewhere in the Bible. A term can first be used literally and later be used figuratively (e.g. "Babylon", Rev. 17:5).

Many commentators draw a parallel with the book of Revelation. They argue that, just as the latter employs figurative language to describe events that are beyond our ability to grasp in detail — events in the distant future, so Genesis uses such language to describe events that were beyond the ability of early readers to grasp in detail — events in the remote past. However, the language of Revelation is more obviously figurative than that of Genesis 1–11 (cf. 1:20 etc.), and its purpose may not have been simplification as discussed later in the chapter.

If God did inspire the author of Genesis to describe creation in a way the ancient Hebrews could understand, the question is, how far did this accommodation extend? Some of the descriptions in the narrative, if taken literally, reflect a primitive conception of the universe. For example:

(1) The sky is described as a solid dome (*rāqîa'*, "firmament", 1:6–8).[3] This term is derived from the verb *rāqa'*, meaning to beat, stamp, or spread, used of the working of metals. The noun seems to imply both expansiveness and rigidity (cf. Job 37:18, "Can you, like him, spread out the skies, strong as a cast metal mirror?").

(2) The sun, moon, and stars are described as being "set in" the dome (1:14–19). If they were thought of as being suspended from it, and the dome as resting on the earth, this would explain the order of creation in 1:1–19 — first the earth, then the sky, then the stars.

(3) The dome is described as having water above it (1:6–7), and trap doors through which this water can rain on to the earth (7:11–12).

These descriptions could indicate that there is considerable accommodation to ancient thought in Genesis. On the other hand, the descriptions could be pictorial, like our word "cloudburst". We do not imagine that clouds are literally balloons of water, but we use this expression, because it vividly describes a heavy downpour of rain. The apparently primitive descriptions in Genesis could have the same status.

Accommodation to ancient thought cannot explain all the differences between the Genesis account of origins and the scientific one. Early

---

[3] See Kidner, *Genesis*, p. 47.

readers would surely have been capable of conceiving of a longer period of creation than six days, and would have expected the sun to have been made before day and night.

Mystification

Figurative language is sometimes used in the Bible to express truths less clearly than they could be expressed literally. For example, after David had committed adultery with Bathsheba, the prophet Nathan told him about a rich man who, to entertain a visitor, did not slaughter one of his own animals, but killed the only one belonging to a poor man (2 Sam. 12:1–4). David immediately condemned the rich man (vv. 5–6), only to find that he had condemned himself ("You are the man!", v. 7).

A second example is Jesus's use of parables. Although it is commonly supposed that Jesus taught in parables in order to make spiritual truths easier to grasp, the reason he himself gave was the opposite of this: it was to make spiritual truths *harder* to grasp, so that only those who really wanted to understand them would be able to do so. This comes out in Luke 8:4–15 (cf. Mat. 13:1–23, Mark 4:1–20). After Jesus had told the crowds a parable (vv. 4–8), his disciples questioned him about it (v. 9). His reply was: "To you it has been given to know the mysteries of the kingdom of God, but to the rest it is given in parables, *that seeing they may not see, and hearing they may not understand*" (v.10; cf. Mat. 13:10–17, Mark 4:10–12). He then explained the parable to them (vv. 11–15).

As a result of teaching in this way, Jesus was quite often misunderstood, his hearers taking literally what he intended figuratively. For example, early in his ministry, the Jews asked him for a sign (John 2:13–22). His answer was "Destroy this temple and in three days I will raise it up" (v. 19). The Jews took this literally, and missed the point (vv. 20–22). Nicodemus made a similar mistake when Jesus told him, "You must be born again" (John 3:1–8), and the disciples when he said, "Lazarus has fallen asleep" (John 11:11–14) and "beware of the yeast of the Pharisees and Sadducees" (Mat. 16:5–12). The disciples expressed great relief when Jesus stopped speaking figuratively (John 16:25–30).

There is an important principle here. God calls us to live by faith (2 Cor. 5:7, etc.). For this he both reveals himself to us in order that faith might be possible, and also hides himself from us (Isa. 45:15) in order that faith might not become sight. There is thus both clarity and obscurity in the Bible. Some things are plain, others are not.

This principle is particularly evident in the case of the Old Testament prophecies concerning the Messiah. To the eyes of faith, these point unmistakably to Jesus of Nazareth. To many of his contemporaries, however, they did not. They are not therefore sufficiently clear to force everyone — even the most hardened scribes and Pharisees — to accept Jesus as Lord, but they are sufficiently clear to assure believers that he is the one of whom the prophets spoke. It is as if God took great care to ensure that the prophecies concerning his son were such that, even when they were being fulfilled, faith was still required to accept him. Jesus himself was certainly very careful not to declare who he was other than in response to faith (Mat. 16:13–20, John 10:22–30, etc.).

The prophecies concerning the last days in the book of Revelation are similar. Most Christians find these very difficult. The wide variety of interpretations of them is a testimony to this. Why are they difficult? Is it because the events being foretold are so far beyond our imagination that they have to be put in a symbolical way? Or is the same principle at work? Are they deliberately obscure, so that, as the events they describe begin to take place, it still requires faith to recognize that what has been foretold is being fulfilled?

One further thought along this line. Daniel was a man who had remarkable visions. These visions were so full of symbolism, and were so difficult to understand, that even Daniel himself could not interpret them. However, when Daniel asked for the interpretation of a vision, God gave it to him (see, e.g., Dan. 7). The question arises, therefore, why was Daniel not given the interpretation in the first place? The answer comes in Daniel 10:12, where he is commended for having "set his heart to understand". The visions were a test of how much he really did want to know what God was saying to him.

In the light of these considerations, the literalness of Genesis 1–11 cannot be pressed too far. In the wisdom of God, there may be more to these chapters than meets the eye. What if God created the universe in the way that science describes, and wanted to reveal this to human beings in such a manner that it would always remain a matter of faith that "the worlds were framed by the word of God" (Heb. 11:3)? He could not then give a completely literal account, otherwise scientists would be able to verify it, and make faith easier. He would be bound to give a more guarded description, couched at least partly in figurative language. To insist on taking the Genesis account completely literally may therefore be going further than God has purposed.

Similar considerations apply to the scientific account. When Russell Stannard suggested to Richard Dawkins that God created animals and human beings by means of evolution, Dawkins replied:[4]

"... The theory of evolution by natural selection is on its own sufficient to explain life. It may be that God on his own is also sufficient to explain life. If I were God I wouldn't do it by evolution! I would do it directly. By invoking the idea of evolution by natural selection as God's way of doing it, you are in effect invoking the one way which makes it look as though God isn't there. So if God chose that way of doing it, then he deliberately chose a way which totally covered his tracks."

To the extent to which it is true that God "deliberately chose a way which totally covered his tracks", the above discussion makes clear why. God does not want to enforce belief. He has accordingly so created the universe that human beings remain free to believe or disbelieve, however much they find out about its origins. This does not mean that he excuses unbelief, since the creation reveals enough of his "eternal power and deity" for belief to be possible (Rom. 1:18–21).[5]

---

[4] Stannard, *Science and Wonders*, pp. 40–41.
[5] Cf. Ferguson, *The Fire in the Equations*.

8 Harmonization of accounts

If the scientific account of origins is correct, the Biblical account can be reconciled to it as indicated in the previous chapter. The Biblical account is taken to describe God's activity in creation in such a way that all generations of human beings can understand it, but need faith to accept it. This requires the description to be at least partly figurative, otherwise later generations would have an advantage over earlier ones. If the account was identical to the scientific one, earlier generations would not be able to understand it, while later generations would be able to confirm it.

If the Biblical account is indeed partly figurative, then the details in it have to be read, not as describing what happened, but as conveying truths underlying what happened. It is these truths which should harmonize with the scientific account if the latter is correct, not the details used to convey them.

This is illustrated by the story Nathan told David (2 Sam. 12:1–4). Taken literally Nathan's story does not describe what David had done. To make the connection with David it is necessary to extract from the details the essence of what happened (a rich man stole from a poor man something that was very precious to him), and then recognize that this is what David had done in committing adultery.

In this chapter I shall apply a similar procedure to Genesis 1–11. I shall first extract the main doctrines from this account, and then relate these to the scientific one. In doing the first, I shall take as my guide the rest of the Bible. Later Biblical writers took Genesis to be authoritative (Mat. 5:17–18, 19:3–6; 2 Tim. 3:16–17; etc.). In any harmonization of the accounts, the teaching they drew from it must be conserved.

8.1 Theology of Genesis

Biblical writers identify the following doctrines in Genesis 1–11.

God (the God of the Bible) created the universe. This is affirmed throughout the Bible. Jesus spoke of God as the Creator (Mat. 19:4–6).

God created the universe in six days, resting on the seventh, thereby setting a pattern for human life. This is stated in the fourth commandment (Exod. 20:8–11):

> [8]Remember the Sabbath day, to keep it holy. [9]Six days you shall labour and do all your work, [10]but the seventh day is a Sabbath to the LORD your God. In it you shall not do any work … [11]For in six days the LORD made the heavens and the earth, the sea, and all that is in them, and he rested on the seventh day. Therefore the LORD blessed the Sabbath day and made it holy.

Jesus explained the value of this commandment (Mark 2:27), while opposing legalistic adherence to it (Mark 2:23–3:6, etc.).

The writer to the Hebrews affirmed that God rested on the seventh day from his work of creating, and is so resting still (Heb. 3:7–4:11).

God created the human race from one man. Paul told the men of Athens, "God who made the world and everything in it … made from one every nation of men to dwell on all the face of the earth" (Acts 17:24–27). "One" is masculine, "one man". Some manuscripts read "one blood". Commentators have traditionally taken the reference to be to Adam.

Man is the image and likeness of God. This is affirmed by Paul (1 Cor. 11:7) and James (Jas. 3:9). Theologians have made various suggestions as to what this description means. Most demur from taking it to include outward appearance, but when Ezekiel saw "the appearance of the likeness of the glory of the LORD" he saw "a likeness in appearance like a man" (Ezek. 1:26–28).[1]

---

[1] Cf. Kidner, *Genesis*, p. 51.

Paul called upon Christians to be "renewed" in the image of God (Eph. 4:20–24, Col. 3:9–10). This implies that man lost some of this image at the Fall. Paul identified what Christians need to regain as "righteousness and true holiness" (Eph. 4:24).

God created a partner for man who would be both equal to him and complementary to him. This was indicated by Jesus (men "marry", women "are given in marriage", both become in the resurrection "equal to the angels and children of God", Luke 20:34–36) and was taught by the apostles (1 Cor. 11:7–12, Gal. 3:28, Eph. 5:22–33, 1 Tim. 2:11–15, 1 Pet. 3:1–7).

God intended marriage to be life-long. When the Pharisees asked Jesus about divorce (Mat. 19:3), he affirmed the teaching of Genesis that God made man and woman such that, when a man marries a woman, they become "one flesh" (vv. 4–5), and concluded, "Therefore what God has joined together, let man not separate" (v. 6).

Human beings are responsible for their actions. This is implied throughout the Bible. The Old Testament teaches that God will render to everyone according to his or her deeds (Job 34:11, Psa. 62:12, Prov. 24:12, etc.). The New Testament affirms this (Mat. 13:47–50, 16:24–27, 25:31–46, etc.).[2] Paul explained how people are culpable for their actions even when they do not know God's law (Rom. 2:14–16). James insisted that no-one can blame God when he or she sins (Jas. 1:13–15).

If human beings are responsible for their actions, they must have freedom to determine these actions. Otherwise they *could* blame God when they sin. Some theologians object that human freedom is incompatible with God's sovereignty, but I have shown elsewhere that this is not the case.[3]

The Devil exists and is wily. The New Testament identifies the Serpent with the Devil (Rev. 12:9, 20:2, cf. John 8:44, 1 John 3:8) and warns against his cunning (2 Cor. 11:3, 14–15, Eph. 6:11–12, 1 Pet. 5:8–9, etc.).

---

[2] On the relationship between this and justification by faith see my book *What is the Gospel?*

[3] Nelson, *God's Control over the Universe*, Sect. 4.

Because Adam sinned, God made human beings subject to death. Paul wrote: "through one man sin entered the world, and through sin death, and so death spread to all men, in that all sinned" (Rom. 5:12). The translation and interpretation of this verse have been much debated.[4] If it is translated as above, Paul's reasoning is that, when God barred the way to the tree of life (Gen. 3:24), he barred it not only to Adam, but to all his descendants who sin. Since all do sin (3:9-26), all therefore die. Paul uses "all" in a general sense, omitting Enoch (Gen. 5:24) and Elijah (2 Kgs. 2:11).

Paul's statement comes in a passage in which he compares and contrasts Adam and Christ (Rom. 5:12–21). He argues that, just as the disobedience of one man brought death to every sinner, so the obedience of one man brings eternal life to every believer. This argument depends on their having been *one* man through whom death came. He makes a similar comparison in 1 Corinthians 15:20–22 and 35–49.

Paul's argument develops the theodicy of Genesis 1–3. God subjected Adam to hardship and death because of his sin. He did this in a way that brought hardship and death, not to Adam only, but also to his descendants. This was because they too sin. God evidently foresaw that they would do this, as I discuss below (Sect. 8.2).

Because Adam sinned, God also made the world a less pleasant place. I discussed this in Chapter 4. While Biblical authors regard some natural evils as having an immediate cause (e.g. the plagues in Egypt, Exod. 7–12; Job's afflictions, Job 1–2), they see others as arising out of the natural order as it now is (e.g. the collapse of a tower, Luke 13:4–5; congenital blindness, John 9:1–3a). Paul wrote that God subjected "the creation" to "futility" and "corruption", as a result of which it "groans and travails", waiting for deliverance (Rom. 8:19–23). Some commentators have suggested that Paul is describing here the state in which God created the universe, but as a Jew, writing to Christians familiar with the Old Testament, he can only be referring to the Curse. Others have suggested that he is describing the result of man's failure to take care of the world (Gen. 1:28), but there is too much "futility" and "corruption" in nature

---

[4] See commentaries.

for this. Biblical writers look forward to a time when there is "a new heaven and a new earth", and "no more curse" (Isa. 65:17–25; Rev. 21:1–5, 22:1–5).

The Bible therefore affirms Genesis's explanation of why there should be natural evil. Some theologians have suggested other explanations,[5] but our task is to preserve the Biblical one.

The Devil will be defeated. Many Christian commentators see in God's words to the Serpent, "her seed ... shall strike[6] your head" (3:15), the first glimpse of the gospel (the "Protevangelium"). The New Testament certainly proclaims the defeat of Satan (Luke 10:18–19, John 12:31, Rom. 16:20, Heb. 2:14–15, Rev. 12:7–9, 20:10, etc.). However, it only relates this to Genesis 3:15 indirectly (Luke 10:18–19, Rom. 16:20). Until the Devil is finally punished (Rev. 20:10) the conflict described in this verse continues.

Because of the great wickedness of Noah's contemporaries, God flooded the world to destroy them, saving only Noah and his family in the ark. Several Biblical writers refer to this event, and draw lessons from it. Jesus used it to warn his disciples to be ready for his return (Mat. 24:36–42). The writer to the Hebrews cited Noah as an exemplar of faith (Heb. 11:7). Peter drew the lessons from it that "the Lord knows how to rescue the godly from trials" (2 Pet. 2:4–9), and that his judgment will certainly come (3:1–13). He also used it as a picture of baptism (1 Pet. 3:20–21).

8.2 Harmonization

Now let us suppose that the scientific account of origins is correct. The aforementioned doctrines can be related to this as follows. I shall take these in a slightly different order from the previous section.

Creation

For a universe to exist, it has to be brought into being. The fact that

---

[5] See, e.g., Adams and Adams (eds.), *The Problem of Evil*; Vardy, *The Puzzle of Evil*; Polkinghorne, *Science and Providence*, Chap. 5; Ward, *God, Chance and Necessity*, Chap. 10.

[6] Hebrew *šûp*. The meaning of this word is uncertain. It occurs only here and in Job 9:17 and Psalm 139:11.

scientists believe that they can describe the evolution of the universe, and trace this back to a beginning, does not alter this. Their description does not secure the universe's existence. Scientists are able to produce descriptions of all kinds of possible universes, but this does not mean that they exist. This is discussed further in Chapter 9.

The Bible affirms that God (the God of the Bible) brought the universe into existence. If the big-bang model is correct, he created the first speck, with whatever structure this had, and its capacity to evolve in the way that it did (Chap. 6). If one of the models that do not have a natural beginning is correct (Chap. 2, Sect. 2.1), he brought the universe into being according to this model, as discussed in Chapter 9. Either way, the universe exists because God made it.

Days of creation

We saw in Chapter 6 that, if the scientific picture is correct, when God devised the universe, he had to decide the laws it would operate on, its starting state, and the sequences that would govern indeterminate events. He then had to bring the universe into being according to this design. After this he could leave it to evolve by itself (until human beings appeared, and he began to interact with them[3]).

If the scientific picture is correct, therefore, the six days in Genesis correspond to the period in which God devised and created the primordial universe (the initial speck on the big-bang model) and drew up the program by which it would evolve. This is the period in which God "worked". The days could have been of 24 hours, or they could have been in God's time (cf. Psa. 90:4, 2 Pet. 3:8). Either way, they indicate that God worked according to the pattern that he subsequently laid down for human beings to work to.

The Fall and the Curse

If the scientific account of the history of the universe is true, right back to the beginning, the Curse corresponds to a change God made in the

---

[3] Nelson, *God's Control over the Universe*, Sect. 4.

design of the universe *before*, or *at the point at which*, he brought it into being.[7] He drew up one design, in which human beings would live in paradisic conditions. Then, foreseeing that the first human beings would rebel against him, he changed the design into one in which they would find life more difficult.

The Bible implies that God foresaw that human beings would sin. The apostles wrote that he planned the salvation of men and women "before the foundation of the world" (Eph. 1:3–14, 1 Pet. 1:17–21; cf. John 17:5, 24). This indicates that he knew that they would sin, if not to the full extent to which they did (Gen. 6:5–7).

Foresight is essential to planning. A motorist who wants to travel from A to B might initially select the most direct route between these two places, then realize that this would take him along some very congested roads, and pick another route to avoid these. God could have changed his design of the universe in a similar way.[8]

Adam and Eve

According to the scientific picture, human beings evolved from hominoid ancestors by mutation and natural selection. If this is correct, it corresponds to the way in which God chose to make them on his *Cursed* design for the universe, with its competition for survival (Chap. 4). He would have made them differently on his original design, which would not have provided the conditions for biological evolution, there being no "struggle for life" as Darwin described it (cf. Gen. 1:29–31).

As Adam and Eve belong to the original design of the universe, they do not necessarily have to appear in the Cursed one. However, as we saw in Chapter 2 (Sect. 2.5), most anthropologists believe that all the human beings in the world today are of one stock, and have a single origin. They envisage that mutations occurred within a population of nearly modern humans to give modern ones. They do not envisage a

---

[7] The first is more likely, but the second is conceivable. It would be like an embryologist changing genes in an embryo.

[8] Cf. MacKay, "The Sovereignty of God in the Natural World", Sect. 4, "The Fallenness of the Natural Order".

single pair of mutants, but there could have been a single pair, God having ordered the mutations to bring this about.

Free will

The question of how, if the universe is as science describes, human beings can have free will, has interested many scientists, secular as well as religious.[9]

Approach (1). Donald MacKay argued that human beings have freedom of action even if the brain operates in a completely determined manner.[10] He showed that, even if a superscientist could predict a decision that a human being would make in the future, he could not communicate this prediction to the human being without making it invalid. MacKay concluded from this that the superscientist's prediction could not be binding on the human being concerned, and that the latter was therefore free to act as he chose.

However, a being whose actions can be predicted by a superscientist can scarcely be reckoned a free agent. If its actions can be predicted scientifically they are determined in advance. If they are determined in advance, the being can say to its maker, "You made me do what I did" (cf. Jas. 1:13–15). MacKay certainly established a necessary condition for freedom of action, but not a sufficient one.

Approach (2). Eddington located human freedom in microscopic processes taking place in the brain, of the kind described by the quantum theory (Chap. 6, Sect. 6.1).[11] According to many scientists, such processes are physically undetermined. Eddington suggested that an agent's choice between two courses of action (A or B) corresponds in the brain to a process of this type, and that the agent determines its outcome. He visualized the process as a change in the state of the brain, to one of two alternatives (a or b).

[9] Cf. Jeeves, *Mind Fields*; *Human Nature at the Millennium*.
[10] MacKay, *Freedom of Action in a Mechanistic Universe*, and other writings.
[11] Eddington, *The Nature of the Physical World*, Chap. 14.

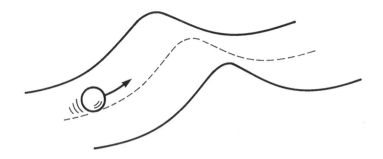

Figure 8.1   A ball rolling up a smooth hump. If the ball has just enough energy to get to the top, there is a bifurcation in its motion at this point.

There are, however, several difficulties with this idea. Firstly, it is not clear how the agent determines the outcome of a quantum change in his brain. Such mechanisms as have been suggested are very speculative.[12] Secondly, the agent is not completely free when repeating the decision because the *distribution* of outcomes of such a change (%a, %b) *is* physically determined (Sect. 6.1). Thirdly, such changes may not be physically undetermined (Sect. 6.1). A possible answer to the second problem is that the brain is never in exactly the same state when a decision is repeated.

Approach (3). John Polkinghorne and others locate human freedom in "bifurcation" points in the working of the brain.[13] Such points commonly arise in physical systems. They are points where only a very slight disturbance leads to a completely different outcome. Suppose, for example, that a ball is rolled up a smooth hump (Fig. 8.1). If the ball does not have sufficient energy to reach the top it will roll back again; if it has more than enough energy to reach the top it will roll over the top and down the other side. If it has just enough energy to reach the top, then when it gets to the top it will stop, and a slight disturbance will make it either roll back again or down the other side.

---

[12]   Zohar, *The Quantum Self*; Tipler, *The Physics of Immortality*, Chap. 7.
[13]   Polkinghorne, *Science and Providence*, and other writings.

Polkinghorne suggests, in essence, that an agent's choice between two courses of action corresponds to a bifurcation in the working of the brain, and that the agent determines the direction the brain takes. However, he does not explain how the agent does this. Disturbances require energy, however small. If the energy is microscopically small, quantum indeterminacy comes into play, and the model becomes the same as the previous one.

Approach (4). Another possibility is that, when an agent is making a free choice, the *contents* of what he is thinking regulate his brain, and determine the course of physical processes in it.[14] This must certainly be the case when an agent is thinking logically. What he thinks is encoded in his brain (cf. Fig. 8.2). Thus his thought in contemplating a problem (T_1), his thoughts in working towards an answer $(T_2, T_3, ...)$, and his thought in arriving at an answer (T_n), are all represented in his brain, and correspond to distinct states of it $(S_1, S_2, S_3, ... S_n)$. So when he is thinking logically, the logic of what he is thinking must determine the sequence of states from S_1 to S_n, otherwise he will get the wrong answer (e.g. if he is calculating 123 + 456 he must get 579). The suggestion is that, when an agent is weighing up different courses of action and deciding between them, the contents of what he is thinking likewise regulate his brain, and determine his decision.

This need not mean that the laws of physics are broken. The human brain could be so constituted as to allow thought-controlled processes to be carried through in it, much as computers are designed to allow programs to be run on them. Computers are physically determined in their operation, but the particular way electricity flows in one is determined by the program being run, and the data put into it. The human brain and sensory system could be so constituted as to allow a child, at a certain stage in its development, to become aware of having to make choices, and to make them as I have described.

There will of course be thought processes in which the determination is reversed, and thoughts are driven by the physics and chemistry of the brain and the body. Many decisions have an emotional or subconscious

---

[14] Nelson, *God's Control over the Universe*, Sect. 4.2.

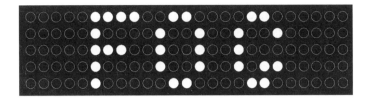

Figure 8.2   Electrical sign encoding a message.

element to them, however they may be presented afterwards. But it remains possible that, when an agent feels free to choose between alternatives, deliberates between them, and makes up his mind on the basis of his considerations (cf. Rom. 2:14–16), his thoughts determine what he decides.

If God's role in the scientific account of origins is as I described in Chapter 6, then on mechanism (2) or (3) he chose not to control the outcome of certain processes in the brain, thereby allowing human beings some freedom to make choices. On mechanism (4) he so designed the universe as to produce human beings with a capacity to make choices. All three mechanisms make human beings responsible for their actions, as the Bible requires.

Other human abilities

On the synthesis I am describing the origin of human abilities that go against natural selection (Chap. 2, Sect. 2.5) resides in God's choice of the course evolution would take. He ensured that the sequence of mutational changes would produce a being that can not only survive as well as humans can, but also do the other things humans can do.

Constitution of human beings: the soul

The sign in Figure 8.2 comprises two things: the machinery of the sign and the content of the message on it. In the same way a human being comprises two things: the machinery of the body (including the brain) and the content of what is encoded in the brain.

Some of what is encoded in the brain is dependent on the body (e.g. the sense of having arms and legs), but some of it is not (e.g. the sense of being answerable to God). The independent part is distinct from the body in the same way that the message in Figure 8.2 is distinct from the battery of lights. Thus this message can be conveyed in a different medium (Fig. 8.3a) or in a different code (Fig. 8.3b) without changing its content. In the same way, the body-independent part of what is encoded in the brain can exist without a body (Eccl. 12:7, Rev. 6:9), or be incorporated into a different kind of body (1 Cor. 15:35–57, 2 Cor. 5:1–4).

Philosophers have long debated whether the immaterial part (IM) of a human being and the material part (M) are dependent or independent, i.e. are two aspects of one thing (monism) or two separate things (dualism).[15] According to the above, IM and M are partly dependent and partly independent. The independent part of IM constitutes the soul.

The Devil

As discussed in Chapter 4, the Serpent in Genesis 3 is one of the animals which God had made (v. 1). He has the ability to deceive Eve, and the freedom to do so (God holds him responsible when he does, v. 14). However, he does not have the power to force Eve to act wrongly (God still holds her responsible for doing so, v. 16). Because of his treachery, God condemns him to a wretched existence (vv. 14–15).

If the scientific account of the origin of the physical universe is correct, this narrative can be understood in two ways.

(1) The Serpent *symbolizes* the Devil. God created a *spiritual* being who, by abusing the freedom God had given him, became the Devil. God designed human beings with the ability to resist the Devil, but foresaw that they would succumb to him, and changed the design of the universe accordingly, as discussed above.

---

[15] See, e.g., articles in Craig (ed.), *Routledge Encyclopedia of Philosophy*; Brown, Murphy, and Malony (eds.), *Whatever Happened to the Soul?*

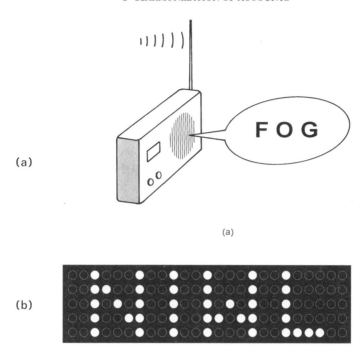

(a)

(a)

(b)

Figure 8.3   Other ways of conveying the message in Figure 8.2. (a) By radio. (b) In another language (Welsh).

(2) In God's first design for the universe the Serpent was an animal —the cleverest animal (v. 1).[16] God foresaw that this would abuse its freedom and succeed in deceiving Adam and Eve. In his revised plan for the universe, he made the Serpent a spiritual being, which would be in hostility with human beings (v. 15).

Of these (1) corresponds to the traditional understanding of the origin of Satan discussed in Chapter 4. (2) makes for a more consistent harmonization of Genesis to science, and better conserves the theodicy of Genesis 1–3.

---

[16]   On the translation of '*ārûm* as "clever" see Chapter 4.

The Flood

If the Flood was a natural event, God designed the universe so that this would happen. This implies that he foresaw how wicked human beings would become, and that Genesis 6:5–8 describes his thoughts as he was devising the universe. Alternatively, he could have brought about the Flood supernaturally, after he had seen how wicked human beings had become (cf. Chap. 10).

Chronology

If the scientific account of origins is correct, the genealogy of Adam in Genesis has to be partly symbolic. Otherwise, scientists would be able to verify it, and make faith easier for later generations than earlier ones, as discussed at the beginning of the chapter. The genealogies in Genesis cannot therefore be expected to give the same date for the creation of Adam as science gives for the origin of *Homo sapiens*.

8.3 Conclusion

I have shown in this chapter that, if the scientific account of origins is correct, the Biblical account can be reconciled to it without loss of authority. Indeed, we have seen that Genesis has been very skilfully composed to communicate the essential truth about the universe, and to make this a matter of faith, for every generation. The claim that God inspired the writing of it is not in any way impaired, it is enhanced.

This conclusion does not mean that the scientific account is correct. As we saw in Chapter 2, the evidence for chemical evolution is weak, and for cosmic and biological evolution inconclusive. The scientific account could be wrong. But if it is right, the Biblical account can be reconciled to it.

My conclusion also does not mean that the whole Bible has the character of the opening chapters of Genesis. Most of it is intended to be taken in the same way by all generations, either literally (e.g. the record of God's dealings with his people, and of the life, death, and resurrection of Jesus) or figuratively (e.g. the visions of Daniel, the parables of Jesus, and the revelation of John).

As I explained in Chapter 6, if the scientific account is correct, this does not diminish God's power and wisdom in creation. If he so designed the components of the universe, disposed them at the beginning, and specified their evolution, that they should generate the universe as we know it, this is no less skilful than constructing the universe as literally described in Genesis.

Part III

Reconciliation of the
Scientific Account of
Origins to the Biblical One

9 Assumptions in scientific account

In this part of the book I shall take the opposite stance from that in the last part. I shall assume that the Biblical account is intended to be taken literally, and consider how far the orthodox scientific account can be reconciled to it without distorting science.

To prepare the ground for this consideration we must first examine some of the assumptions on which the scientific account is based.

9.1 Continuous correspondence between theory and reality

The first assumption is that there is a continuous correspondence between scientific models of reality and reality itself.

Consider, for example, the big-bang model. This is based on astronomical observations that suggest that the universe is expanding (Chap. 2, Sect. 2.1). By extrapolating this expansion backwards scientists calculate that the universe had a vanishingly small volume about 10–15 billion years ago, and infer from this that it started in a huge explosion. However, extrapolating the expansion backwards in this way presupposes that the universe has been in existence throughout the period involved. This is not necessarily the case.

Some illustrations will make this clear:

(1) Suppose that you turn on the radio and hear an orchestra playing the end of Elgar's well-known "Pomp and Circumstance" march ("March No. 1"). By extrapolating back from this you might infer that about six minutes earlier they were playing the opening bars of this march. However, this assumes that they started at the

beginning. They could have been playing the finale on its own, in which case they would only have been playing for about a minute when you turned the radio on.

(2) Imagine arriving late at a theatre and taking your seat in the middle of a play. By watching the rest of the play, you can gradually piece together something of what has gone before. Apparently some important papers had been stolen from a country home, a policeman who had been put on the case had been attacked, and now a private detective is trying to solve the mystery. What you cannot work out, however, is how much of this has been acted out on the stage, and how much has been left to the audience to imagine. Did scene 1 begin before the robbery, after the robbery and before the attack on the policeman, or after the attack on the policeman? There is simply no way of answering these questions on the basis of the part of the play that you see.

(3) Imagine that you are standing on Bletchley railway station. At about 11.30 a.m. an express train passes through heading north. Knowing that such trains take about 30 minutes to reach Bletchley from London, you infer that this must have been the 11.00 a.m. from Euston. However, this presupposes continuous correspondence between train and timetable all the way back to London. It is possible that, on the day in question, because of engineering work between Euston and Watford, the train started at Watford at the correspondingly later time of 11.10 a.m. The time through Bletchley would be just the same.

(4) Consider two identical spring-driven clocks. One is wound up and started. After it has been running for some time, the second is given the same number of turns as are left on the first clock, and set running. The two clocks cannot now be distinguished. To anyone who has not witnessed the history of the second clock, it looks as if it has been running for as long as the first.

Thus, even if the big-bang model of the universe is mathematically correct, this does not necessarily mean that the universe was created 10–15 billion years ago. It could equally well have been created very much more recently than this, with a volume close to its present volume, and expanding at its present rate. The fact that a mathematical model makes the universe appear to have a long history does not mean that the universe itself has such a history.

This conclusion applies also to models of the universe that do not have a beginning (Chap. 2, Sect. 2.1). On these models, the universe still has to be created (be brought into being), and the point at which it is marks its actual beginning, even if afterwards it appears as if it did not have one (just as a pendulum, once set swinging, looks as if it has always been swinging).

The distinction between model and reality is recognized by Stephen Hawking when he writes, in respect of a possible unified theory of the universe:[1]

Even if there is only one possible unified theory, it is just a set of rules and equations. What is it that breathes fire into the equations and makes a universe for them to describe? The usual approach of science of constructing a mathematical model cannot answer the questions of why there should be a universe for the model to describe. Why does the universe go to all the bother of existing? Is the unified theory so compelling that it brings about its own existence? Or does it need a creator, and, if so, does he have any other effect on the universe? And who created him?

The distinction between mathematical model and reality cannot be stressed enough. There is a tendency to think that, because the development of the universe can be traced back over a long period of time, the universe must have been in existence for this period of time. This is a mistake. There is no scientific reason at all why God, if he only wanted the universe to be in existence for the period of human history, should not have brought it into being at the beginning of this period.

[1] Hawking, *A Brief History of Time*, p. 174.

9.2 Fixity of natural law and complete conformity to it

Science is made possible by the fact that natural phenomena display regularities. The sun always rises in the east, apples always fall downwards, candles always get shorter when they burn, mice always die when they are deprived of air. Scientists study these regularities, summarize them in the form of laws, and devise theories to explain them.

Now in building up their picture of the history of the universe, scientists make two important assumptions:

➤ (I) the universe has conformed to the same laws throughout its history,

➤ (II) nothing has ever happened contrary to these laws.

Assumption (I) is a big one to make, as the following analogies show.

(1) Imagine again that you turn on the radio and hear an orchestra playing the finale of Elgar's "Pomp and Circumstance" march. You might infer from this that, whether they were playing the whole march or just the finale, they were playing this composition throughout. However, this inference could be wrong. The orchestra could have been playing a medley of music, as in BBC Radio 4's "UK Theme".

(2) Suppose that you are given a new mechanical clock. You find that it keeps good time. You might infer from this that it has always kept good time, from when it left the factory. It is possible, however, that the person who gave it to you found that it did not keep good time, and had it adjusted before giving it to you. Your inference that it has always kept good time would then be wrong.

(3) Imagine that you see someone tiling a wall according to a particular pattern (Fig. 9.1c). You may suppose that he tiled the wall according to this pattern from the start. But it is possible that he started tiling according to a different pattern (Fig. 9.1a). Not liking this, he replaced some of the tiles to produce a new pattern (Fig. 9.1b), and continued tiling according to this.

(4) I once saw at an exhibition a model railway operated by a computer. The trains ran to a timetable that repeated itself at intervals. Anyone

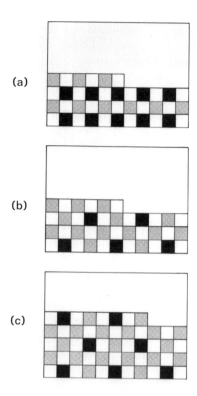

Figure 9.1 (a) Tiling a wall according to a particular pattern. (b) Changing this pattern by replacing some of the black tiles by shaded ones. (c) Continuing to tile according to the new pattern.

who watched the trains for long enough could accordingly work out this timetable, and predict future movements on this basis. However, this does not mean that trains had always run, and would always run, to this timetable. The model-maker who built the layout could change the program if he wanted to.

In the same way, God can change the way the universe works if he wants to. If it now runs according to certain laws, this is because he has made it run according to these laws. As its creator, he always has the power to change the laws.

Assumption (II) (complete conformity to natural law) is also a big one to make. If God created the universe, he has the power to make things happen in it supernaturally. No-one would suggest that the model-maker in illustration (4) cannot intervene in the operation of his model railway. The universe is God's workmanship: he can do to it whatever he wills.

Thus God *could* have done what the Bible describes — he could have created the universe in six days, he could have changed the natural order after the Fall, and he could have brought a flood upon the earth (Chap. 4). There is nothing in science to gainsay this. Scientists can only describe the natural order as it is now: they cannot say anything about how this order has come about.

Christians should not doubt that God can change the universe in any way he wants. Jesus chided the Sadducees for not believing in the resurrection (Mat. 22:23–33). He told them, "You err because you do not know the Scriptures or the power of God" (v. 29). Peter warned against those who questioned Jesus's return, and the promise of a new heaven and a new earth (2 Pet. 3:1–13). They argued that "everything continues as it has since the beginning of creation" (v. 4). Peter countered by reminding them of God's power in Creation and the Flood (vv. 5-6). God has the ability to change the natural order, whose order it is.

If God did do what the Bible describes, then the universe only acquired its present order after the Fall or the Flood (depending on whether the latter was natural or supernatural). However, because it is running according to laws, it appears as if it has always had this order. Scientists can extrapolate the history of the universe back on the basis of these laws to before the Fall or the Flood. Indeed they can extrapolate it right back to a big bang, as they do. However, prior to the Fall or Flood the history is imaginary (cf. Sect. 9.1). It describes what the universe would have been like if it had had the order it now has, but not what it was actually like.

This can be illustrated by the analogies used earlier in this section. For example, the time given by your new clock in (2) can be extrapolated back on the basis of its present time-keeping to before your friend had it adjusted. The times would be wrong for the period prior to the adjustment, but they would accurately reflect how your clock is working now, being the times it would have given in the earlier period if it had performed then as it does today.

10 Harmonization of accounts

If the assumptions in the scientific picture of the universe are relaxed, as described in the preceding chapter, the scientific account of origins can be reconciled to the Biblical one as follows.

10.1 Outline

Creation

Suppose that God did create the universe in six days a few thousand years ago. Then, as discussed in Section 9.1, by day 7 it would have been a going concern. The distant galaxies (if astronomers are right) would have been moving away from each other, the earth would have had smooth rocks and pebbles on it, trees would have had rings, and so on.

On day 7, therefore, the universe would have appeared to have had a history that it did not in reality have.[1] If Adam had been a scientist, he could have drawn up a scientific description of its operation which he could have extrapolated back to before day 7. This description would have accurately reflected the design of the universe, but would not have corresponded to reality before day 7.

As created the universe would have been in an uncursed state. It would have had none of the features that disfigure it now (Chap. 4).

Fall and Curse

Suppose now that God changed the natural order after the Fall, and carried this change through fully, so that everything in the universe became

---

[1] Cf. Chateaubriand, *Génie du Christianisme*, Part 1, Book 4, Chap. 5 (1802); Penn, *A Comparative Estimate of the Mineral and Mosaical Geologies* (1822); Gosse, *Omphalos* (1857).

consistent with the new order, as in the tiling illustration in the previous chapter (Fig. 9.1, p. 121). A new scientific picture of the universe now applies. This picture can be extrapolated back to before the Fall, but the actual history before the Fall was different, as discussed in Section 9.2.

According to the traditional understanding of Genesis, the natural order changed very radically after the Fall (Chap. 4). This will have entailed substantial remodelling of the earth. I discuss this further below.

Flood

If God flooded the earth supernaturally, there will have been a further change in the natural order at the time of this event. Even if the laws of nature are the same after the Flood as before it, the condition of the world after the Flood will be different from what it would have been if the Flood had not taken place. In this circumstance, what I have said about the Fall applies again to the Flood. Our scientific picture of the world relates to its post-Flood state, and only describes reality back to the Flood. Extrapolation to times earlier than this tells us what the world would have been like if it had possessed its present design at earlier times, but not what it was actually like.

10.2 Details

These ideas raise a number of detailed questions, which I shall now consider.

Operation of the universe during creation

If God created the universe over a period of six days, how did it operate during this period? It could not have operated according to the laws it did on day 7. These imply a different order of creation, e.g. of the sun before day and night.

There are several possible answers to this. One is that God operated the universe himself (cf. Rev. 22:5) until he had completed it. A second is that he made the universe run according to different laws on different days, and changed the laws as he proceeded. For example, he could have designed the universe so that on days 1–3 the earth would rotate and a diffuse light illuminate it, and then developed the design so that on day 4 there would be a sun, moon, and stars.

Starlight

If God created the universe a few thousand years ago, why is it possible to see stars that are more than a few thousand light years away? The light from such stars will not yet have had time to reach the earth.

The answer to this question must be that, when God created the stars, he also created the light emanating from them. All the stars would then be visible from the earth from the moment they were created.

This idea is not as artificial or contrived as it may seem. A mature creation is a mature creation. From a scientific point of view, the universe is a complex whole, with an event in one region affecting behaviour in another. Recent calculations have shown that the universe is an extremely sensitive system in this respect: even a very small event can have a significant effect, even at a great distance from it.[2] Thus, for any part of the universe to be created in a particular state, every other part has to be created in accordance with this state.

Radioactivity

Similar considerations apply to radioactive substances. If God created other parts of the universe in a mature state, then he also created these in a mature (i.e. partly decayed) state. Maturity of creation means maturity of everything in it. If Adam had been capable of carrying out radiometric measurements, he would have concluded that the rocks around him were older than they were, just as he would have concluded that other things around him (pebbles, trees, etc.) were older than they were.

I am assuming that radioactivity formed part of the original creation and not of the "corruption" God introduced at the Fall. If he did introduce radioactivity at the Fall, then he changed the whole design of the universe

---

[2] Denbigh and Denbigh, *Entropy in Relation to Incomplete Knowledge*, pp. 32–33.

at this point, from one in which there was no radioactivity on the earth to one in which there is. If he carried this change through consistently, the earth would then have been in a mature state according to its *new* design, with all the radioactive substances partly decayed.

Similarities between organisms

If God created different kinds of organism separately as described in Genesis 1, then he made them with chemical similarities between them, so that plants could provide food for animals and the biosphere function as an integrated whole. If he subsequently changed the natural order after the Fall and the Flood, he did so in such a way that organisms continued to be chemically similar to each other. Only if they are can the biosphere function in the way that it does.

Fossils

If God created plants and animals a few thousand years ago, why should there be fossilized remains dating from before this? In particular, why should there be the remains of species which, if the earth is only a few thousand years old, have never existed (e.g. dinosaurs)? And why should there be such vast quantities of fossilized material (chalk, coal, oil, etc.)?

The answer to these questions is, once again, that, if the universe is to conform to a particular design, all the features of that design must be present. If the design is such that, had the universe been in existence for longer than a few thousand years, fossils would have been formed prior to this date, then, when the universe is brought into conformity with this design, the earth must have fossils in it. Otherwise, the universe fails to conform completely to the design.

At what stage did the earth acquire its apparently ancient fossils — when it was created or after the Fall? The answer to this depends on the stage at which the death of animals began (for an animal to be fossilized it has to die). As I discussed in Chapter 4, Biblical commentators are divided over when this was.

No animal death before Fall

On the view that the death of animals (at least of higher animals) came into the world after the Fall (Chap. 4), God changed the design of the universe at this point, from one in which no fossils would be formed (at least of higher animals) into one in which many would be. To make the universe conform completely to the new design, he therefore had to remodel, not only the animals living at the time, but also rocks and landscapes, bringing in the fossils that would have been formed if the earth had always had this design.

This necessity may be illustrated as follows. Imagine a film-director making a science-fiction film about the discovery of an alien settlement in a remote part of China and the war that this precipitates. His first idea is that the aliens should be immortal (plot 1), and he writes the script, builds the set, and starts shooting on this basis. He then decides to make the aliens mortal (plot 2), so he rewrites the script, adds to the set a cemetery, and starts filming again. The cemetery contains the remains of aliens who lived and died *before* the film begins, but their inclusion is necessary if the film is to accord completely with plot 2.

Any change to a system that is carried through consistently will produce artefacts of that change. This is illustrated by the Second Coming. According to Paul, when Jesus comes again, believers who have died will be raised, while those who are living on the earth at the time will be changed into the same state (1 Thes. 4:13–18, 1 Cor. 15:35–57). The latter will accordingly appear as if they have died and been raised like the former, even though they will not have done. This is the inevitable consequence of carrying the transformation of believers through consistently.

Paul says that, at the Second Coming, believers living on the earth will be changed "in a moment" (1 Cor. 15:51–52). God could likewise have changed the earth after the Fall "in a moment".

My thesis that God carried changes in the natural order through consistently avoids the problem raised by Davis Young of not knowing which parts of the earth's crust science applies to.[3] Science applies to all

---

[3] Young, *Creation and the Flood*, Chap. 3.

parts, and correctly delineates the history the earth would have had if it had conformed to its present design throughout. Scientists may be disturbed by the idea that much of this history is only apparent, but what they are looking at is really the present design of the universe, not its history.

Deception?

If God furnished rocks with fossils after the Fall, human beings are mistaken when they find these fossils and take them to be of creatures that once existed. Does this not make God a deceiver?

This question can be answered in two ways:

(1) Whether parts of the created order after the Fall could have continued to conform to the pre-Curse design depends on the compatibility between this design and the post-Curse one. It would not be possible, for example, to have some parts of the natural world conforming to one set of laws, and other parts conforming to another set, as they would clash where they came in contact (just as it would not be possible to have some parts of the world made up of ordinary matter and other parts made up of antimatter, since these are converted into radiation when they come in contact). If the Curse was as radical as the Bible implies, the two designs could have been incompatible, in which case God had to change the whole created order, including the rocks.[4]

(2) Even if God did not have to do this, he may have wished to make "the whole creation" display the Curse (cf. Rom. 8:22), and show to human beings the seriousness of sin (cf. Deut. 29:18–28).

Other scenarios

On the view that animal death formed part of the original creation, and predation and disease came in after the Fall, God created the earth with fossils in it, and changed some of them after the Fall (many fossils are of predators, and some show signs of disease). God's actions are again

---

[4] Cf. MacKay, "The Sovereignty of God in the Natural World", Sect. 4, "The Fallenness of the Natural Order".

explained by the need for the earth to conform fully to the design that it has at any stage.

Some Biblical Christian scientists have argued that most of the fossils in the earth's crust were formed naturally in the Flood and subsequent events (Chap. 2, Sect. 2.6). Few professional geologists, however, accept this.

Adam and Eve

As we have seen, most anthropologists currently believe that all the human beings in the world today are of one stock, and have a single origin (Chap. 2, Sect. 2.5). They locate this origin in Africa, but as discussed in Section 2.5, it could have been elsewhere. However, they date the origin around 200,000 years ago, whereas, if the genealogies in Genesis 5 and 11 are complete, the Bible dates it around 4000 or 5000 B.C. (Chap. 4, Table 4.3). This discrepancy can be removed in two ways:

(1) by taking the genealogies to be incomplete, as we saw in Chapter 4 is possible;

(2) by supposing that, when God changed the design of the universe after the Fall, he not only changed the design of Adam and Eve, but brought other human beings into existence in accordance with this design.

Of these (1) makes 200,000 B.P. the actual date of origin, (2) the apparent date.

Some anthropologists currently believe that modern humans have a multiregional origin (Sect. 2.5). If this turns out to be scientifically correct, then (2) would apply.

On (1) God would have had to bring into existence at the Fall any non-Adamite humans that would have still been living in 200,000 B.P. on the post-Fall design of the universe. Anthropologists currently believe that some *Homo* species overlapped with *Homo sapiens* before becoming extinct (Sect. 2.5).

Pre-Adamite human remains

Pre-Adamite human remains pose a similar problem to fossils. Given that such remains occur, they do so because, if the universe had had the design before the Fall that it had afterwards, there would have been pre-Adamites living and dying on the earth. Their remains had therefore to be included in the remodelled earth after the Fall, if this was to be consistent with its new design. This applies not only to bones, but also to artefacts. It also applies to non-Adamite remains predating the Fall.

The Devil

According to Genesis 3 the Serpent was an animal (Chap. 4). The New Testament, however, identifies the Serpent as the Devil (Rev. 12:9, 20:2). If Genesis 3 is taken literally, therefore, this identification implies that the spirit of the Serpent lived on after the death of its body (Chap. 4).

The Flood

As we saw in Chapter 4, the Flood could have been local, widespread, or global. If the genealogy in Genesis 11 is complete, the episode occurred around 3000 B.C. (Table 4.3).

I discussed evidence for the Flood in Chapter 5. There is no evidence of widespread or global flooding around 3000 B.C., so if the Flood did take place at this time, it was almost certainly local. There is some evidence of widespread flooding prior to 3000 B.C. An earlier date would require the genealogy in Genesis 11 to be incomplete, which is possible (Chap. 4).

10.3 Scientific status

There is nothing in the above harmonization to conflict with modern science. The latter, if it is correct, accurately describes the present order in the universe, and the history implied by this order. That the actual history prior to the Flood or the Fall should be different from this is not unscientific. The scientific history of any system becomes unreal prior to a change in the system. If a pendulum is set swinging with a certain amplitude, and at some later time its amplitude is changed, a scientific history based on its later motion becomes unreal prior to the change in motion.

The possibility that much of the history of the universe is only apparent has been raised by a correspondent to the scientific journal *Nature*:[5]

> If God was smart enough to create The System, he was certainly smart enough to cover his tracks; that is he could have 'implanted' the geological astronomical record so that what many of us now see as a scientifically pre-Creation history is merely a divine artefact.
>
> I say this as a non-creationist scientist who nevertheless cannot find a way around this argument. Can you? If not, then science would also appear to be a religion: we simply believe there was no relatively recent Creation but cannot prove it.

Although the writer makes God's actions seem contrived (I have shown that God had to "implant" the geological and astronomical record to make the universe completely consistent with its design), he nevertheless grasps the essential point.

More recently, Professor R. E. M. Hedges, director of the Radiocarbon Accelerator Unit at Oxford, replying to John Miles, a believer in a young earth, wrote:[6]

> I can see no other way — if Miles is to reconcile the scientific evidence [for the age of the earth] with his prior belief — than for him to believe that the creation of the world, whenever it was, included all the necessary indications, in a consistent way, that it is at least several billion years old.

This is my thesis here.

---

[5] Denness, "Divine Artefact".
[6] Hedges, "Dated Theory in a Flux?"

10.4 Conclusion

In the last two chapters I have shown that the scientific account of origins can be reconciled to a literal reading of Genesis without having to distort either. This does not mean that Genesis should be read literally, but it does mean that there is no scientific reason why it should not be.

Part IV

Conclusions

11 Conclusions

11.1 Reconcilability

In Part II I showed that the Biblical account of origins can be reconciled to the scientific one without weakening the Bible's authority. In Part III I have shown that the scientific account can be reconciled to a literal reading of the Biblical one without distorting science. The two accounts are therefore capable of being harmonized — there is no irresolvable conflict between them.

This conclusion takes the pressure off the question of the relationship between science and the Bible. If the scientific account is correct, Genesis can be reconciled to it; if a literal reading of Genesis is correct, science can be reconciled to this. There is no need to try to prove one against the other.

This leaves Christian scientists free to consider evolutionary and anti-evolutionary theories of origins on their merits, and to call upon other scientists to do the same. There is a need for scientists who are prepared to consider both evolutionary and anti-evolutionary ideas, and to appraise the evidence for them impartially. As we saw in Chapter 2, the case for evolution is not as strong as is commonly supposed.

Similar considerations apply to the interpretation of Genesis: scholars are free to consider the choice between literal and figurative readings on their merits. They can also work on other ways of harmonizing science and the Bible without the credibility of the Bible being at stake.

11.2 Mystery

Where the truth lies between my syntheses is uncertain. On the evidence that we have, either could be the true picture, or anything in between. Our ignorance, whether we be scientists or interpreters of the Bible, greatly exceeds our knowledge. We can say that God made the universe, but exactly how he did so we cannot be sure.

This is not as unsatisfactory as it may appear. God is God, we are but creatures. If, as we study those things that lie on the fringes of what God has clearly revealed to us, in nature or the Bible, we find ourselves groping, this is no bad thing. It trims us down to size; it puts us in our place. There is no greater need in the modern world than that men and women should humble themselves before God. "The fear of the LORD", the Bible says, "is the beginning of wisdom" (Prov. 9:10).

As Christians we should not feel ourselves to be under pressure to have answers to *all* the questions people ask. Our message to the world is that God has spoken, not that he has told us everything. Our testimony is that we have come to know him through Jesus Christ, not that we have come to know him fully. Moses spoke both of what God had revealed to the children of Israel and of what he had not: "The secret things belong to the LORD our God, but the things that are revealed belong to us" (Deut. 29:29). Paul said, "I know whom I have believed" (2 Tim. 1:12), but also: "we know in part, and we prophesy in part … For now we see through a glass, darkly" (1 Cor. 13:8–12);[1] "O the depth of the riches of the wisdom and knowledge of God! How unsearchable are his judgments, and his ways past finding out" (Rom. 11:33–36). We need not be ashamed about what we do not know or understand. Our humble "not knowing" glorifies God as much as our thankful "knowing". Indeed, if we are to commend God's call to people in the world to repent and to turn humbly to him, we need to be humble ourselves.

11.3 Tolerance

In view of the difficulty in deciding where the truth about origins lies, Christians should be careful about how they treat each other over this issue. Some sincerely believe that the scientific account is correct and

---

[1] Authorized Version. Lit. "we see by a mirror in a riddle". Ancient mirrors did not reflect very well.

that Genesis should be taken figuratively; others sincerely believe that Genesis should be taken literally. Let each respect the conviction of the other (cf. Rom. 14:1–15:13).

Del Ratzsch has called for more dialogue between the two sides on the issue.[2] He is surely right. But let there not be too much discussion. True religion is not to engage in endless controversy, but to visit orphans and widows in their affliction, and to keep oneself unstained from the world (1 Tim. 1:3–4, Jas. 1:26–27).

11.4 Certainties

Although we may not be sure how literally the early chapters of Genesis should be taken, we need have no uncertainty about what they are teaching. They tell us

- that God made the universe (1:1–2:3);
- that he made man in his own image (1:26–27);
- that he gave man the task of looking after the earth (1:28);
- that he made woman to be "a helper suitable for him" (2:18–24);
- that man and woman disobeyed him (2:16–17, 3:1–7);
- that he punished them for this, making life harder for them (3:16–19), and bringing upon them death (3:22–24);
- that he continues to hold men and women responsible for their actions (4–11);
- that the devil continues to try to stop them from doing what is right (3:14–15).

This teaching sets out the human situation as it now is, and lays a foundation for the rest of the Bible. It is against this background that Jesus came into the world to defeat the devil (John 12:31), conquer death (1 Cor. 15. Heb. 2:14–15), re-create men and women (John 3:1–16, 2 Cor. 5:17), and prepare the way for "a new heaven and a new earth" (Rev. 21:1–5). If the Curse is the Bible's explanation of suffering in nature, its removal is the Bible's hope (Rom. 8:18–25, Rev. 22:1–5).

[2] Ratzsch, *The Battle of Beginnings.*

Update

Chapter 2 Scientific account of origins

2.1 Big bang and cosmic evolution

Recent work has confirmed that there are variations in the weak background radiation in space, and that the expansion of the universe is accelerating, requiring the introduction of the "cosmological constant" referred to in the text.[1] This constant implies that there is an additional energy in the universe ("dark energy") which cosmologists also have to explain.

Other models

In a recent book, Stephen Hawking espouses a multi-universe theory.[2] I discuss theories of this type in Chapter 6.

2.3 Chemical evolution: the origin of life

This continues to be a mystery. A rover on Mars is currently looking for evidence of conditions conducive to life.

2.4 Biological evolution

In the DNA of higher organisms, there are long sections that do not

---

[1] See, e.g., Ryden, *Introduction to Cosmology*; Hawley and Holcomb, *Foundations of Modern Cosmology*.
[2] Hawking and Mlodinow, *The Grand Design*.

function as genes. It is now known that these function as switches, turning genes on and off.[3] This further complicates the task of explaining biological evolution in terms of step-wise changes in DNA.

To reference 24, add: Behe, *The Edge of Evolution: the Search for the Limits of Darwinism*. To reference 34, add: Shapiro, *Evolution: a View from the 21st Century*.

2.5 Origin of human beings

This continues to be a difficult problem.[4] Note that the difference in nucleide sequences between chimpanzees and humans, though only 1–2%, still amounts to 30–60 million pairs (Table 2.3). The difference is particularly marked for the Y chromosome.[5]

2.6 Alternative sciences

Progressive creation science

The concept of "intelligent design" (ID) has become very popular.[6] The idea derives from the work of Michael Behe I discussed in the text (p. 22), and from the writings of William Dembski.[7] Behe argued that some biological systems have a complexity that cannot be accounted for by a step-wise evolutionary mechanism ("irreducible" complexity), which points to these systems having been designed. Dembski comes to a similar conclusion on probabilistic grounds. As I explained in the text, however, such complexity could still arise by a step-wise mechanism, if the last of a series of otherwise neutral mutations brings them all into play. It could alternatively arise by a process involving big mutations as some have suggested (ref. 34).

[3] See Pennisi, "ENCODE Project Writes Eulogy for Junk DNA".

[4] See, e.g., Lewin, *Human Evolution*; McKee, Poirier, and McGraw, *Understanding Human Evolution*; Stringer and Andrews, *The Complete World of Human Evolution*; Cela-Conde and Ayala, *Human Evolution*.

[5] Hughes *et al.*, "Chimpanzee and Human Y Chromosomes Are Remarkably Divergent in Structure and Gene Content".

[6] For a recent exposition, see Dembski and Witt, *Intelligent Design Uncensored*.

[7] See Bibliography, Supplement.

Literal Biblical creation science

To reference 51 add:

- Byl, *God and Cosmos*
- Nevin (ed.), *Should Christians Embrace Evolution?*
- Garner, *The New Creationism*

As the last title implies, there have been some big changes in this kind of science. Some old ideas have been discarded, and some new ones brought in.

An important new idea is that the conventional radiometric ages of rocks are wrong because rates of radioactive decay were very much higher in the past, as evidenced by[8]

(1) systematic differences in the ages obtained for the same rock by different methods;

(2) higher concentrations of helium gas in a uranium-containing mineral (zircon) than expected from the amount of decay of uranium in the mineral and the rate of diffusion of helium out of it (uranium gives off helium when it decays);

(3) the formation of halos in rocks by the decay of radioactive atoms that are not normally produced quickly enough to accumulate in sufficient quantities to form halos.

The big problem with this idea is that radioactive decay generates heat, and there are no signs in the rocks of very much higher rates of heating in the past.[9] In respect to (1)–(3),

- there are many possible reasons for the differences in (1);
- the expectation in (2) is based on a simple model of diffusion which may not apply;[10]
- there could be a defect in the rock in (3) trapping the atoms concerned.

---

[8] See DeYoung, *Thousands not Billions*; Garner, *The New Creationism*, Chap. 6.
[9] On attempts to get round this problem, see Boudreaux and Baxter, *God Created the Earth*, Part 2.
[10] See Loechelt, "Fenton Hill Revisited: the Retention of Helium in Zircons and the Case for Accelerated Nuclear Decay".

Relative Time

Humphreys' approach is referred to as "white hole cosmology". He has developed this further in Vardiman and Humphreys, "A New Creationist Cosmology".

Flood geology

Carol Hill has drawn attention to a serious problem with the idea that most sedimentary rocks were formed in the Flood.[11] This is that, while the author of Genesis describes the Tigris and Euphrates before the Flood as if his readers knew them (2:10–14), these rivers flow today through the Mesopotamian plain over layers of sedimentary rock thousands of feet thick. Before these were laid, the rivers in the region would have been very different. Further, Noah correctly anticipated that a dove would find olive trees growing after the waters had subsided (8:8–11). There could not therefore have been a major reworking of the earth's crust in the Flood.

Chapter 3 Biblical account of origins

Section 3.3 Sources

A popular variant of the thesis that the author of Genesis adapted pagan epics is that he wrote it as a polemic against the ideas expressed in these epics.[12] Again, however, this presupposes that the author wrote it *after* people had acquired these ideas, whereas he could have composed it before this.

---

[11] Hill, "The Garden of Eden: a Modern Landscape". (Note that her location of Eden is different from mine.)

[12] See, e.g., Lucas, *Can We Believe Genesis Today?*; Currid, *Genesis*, Vol. 1, pp. 43–51.

Chapter 4 Literal meaning of Genesis

Genesis1: Creation

In a recent book, John Walton argues that Genesis 1, read as its first readers would have read it, is not about God making things out of nothing, but about him giving them function (e.g. giving light and darkness — day and night — the role of marking time).[13] The text does not, however, support this. For example, 1:3–5 describes the creation of light as light ("And God said, 'Let there be light,' and there was light. And God saw that the light was good").[14] Only then does it describe God creating function ("And God separated the light from the darkness. And God called the light 'day', and the darkness he called 'night'").

Walton goes on to suggest that Genesis 1 is about God preparing for himself a cosmic temple in which to dwell. Genesis 3, however, implies that God went away from Adam and Eve after he had set them in the garden, only coming back to them after they had sinned (v. 8).

The "days"

Further references:

- Ref. 9: Collins, *Genesis 1–4*, Chap. 4; Poythress, *Redeeming Science*, Chap. 10. These writers take the "days" of God's work as being *analogous* to the days of human work. See also Ross, *A Matter of Days*.
- Ref. 12: Lennox, *Seven Days that Divide the World*.

---

[13] Walton, *The Lost World of Genesis One*
[14] Walton takes *'ôr* ("light") to mean "a period of light" (*Lost World*, pp. 53–55), but this is not its usual meaning, and does not remove the difficulty.

Genesis 2 and 3: Adam and Eve, the Fall and the Curse

Walton points out that, since Adam's immortality depended on him eating from the tree of life, God created him mortal.[15] But God's intention was that he should be immortal[16] — God put him in a garden and told him that he could eat from "every tree in the garden" except for the tree of the knowledge of good and evil (2:15–17). "Every tree" included the tree of life (2:8–9). Note also what happened to Enoch (5:24).

An interpretation of the Curse that has become very popular is that it affected relations between the parties involved, but left the natural order otherwise unchanged.[17] On this interpretation,

(1) "death" in the passage refers exclusively to spiritual death;

(2) "good" in Genesis 1 means "fit for purpose" — God's purpose being the creation of a challenging world in which humans beings can develop character;

(3) physical death is, in this sense, "very good";

(4) so likewise are predation, disease, earthquakes, etc.

While there are certainly indications in the narrative that the Curse affected relationships — between Eve and the Serpent (3:15) and between Adam and Eve (3:16b) — this interpretation strains the text, and does not cohere with the rest of the Bible.[18]

Relation between Genesis 1 and 2

A popular interpretation of Genesis 1–2 today is that Genesis 1 is about the creation of anatomically human beings and that Genesis 2 describes God calling a couple of these into fellowship with him. They thereby become fully spiritual beings (designated *Homo divinus*) and federal

---

[15] *Lost World*, pp. 98–100.

[16] Cf. Collins, *Genesis 1–4*, pp. 160–162; *Did Adam and Eve Really Exist?*, pp. 115–116.

[17] See, e.g., Berry, "This Cursed Earth"; Bimson, "Reconsidering a 'Cosmic Fall'"; Alexander, *Creation or Evolution*, Chaps. 11–13; Collins, *Genesis 1–4*, Chap. 6; Hitchcock, "'Good Death'"; Lucas, "God and 'Natural Evil'".

[18] See Section 8.1 and my article, "Genesis 1–3 as a Theodicy".

leaders of the human race.[19] This interpretation, however, breaks the relationship between Genesis 1 and 2 that I explained in the text.[20]

To reference 18 in the text, add Collins, "The *wayyiqtol* as 'Pluperfect'".

Eden

Scholars have tried to identify the Pishon and the Gihon with particular rivers having their headwaters on the highland plateau north of Mesopotamia. The most convincing is the identification of the Gihon with the Arexes/Aras, which flows into the Caspian Sea.[21] This river was once called the Gaihun.

Locating Eden in this region does not go against the bearing in 2:8 ("east" of Canaan) since, in Genesis, north-east is still called "east" (see 29:1 referring to the people living around Haran).

Recent work suggests another possible identification of Eden. This is with the land area that existed before sea levels rose after the last Ice Age and flooded the basin that now forms the Persian Gulf. This basin was watered mainly by the Tigris, Euphrates, Karun, and Wadi Batin Rivers, which came together to form the Ur-Schatt River, now under the sea.[22] The Karun runs down the mountains east of the Tigris, through an area Speiser identified as the Cush of 2:13.[23] The Wadi Batin comes in from Arabia in the west, a country that was noted for its gold and called Havilah in 25:18.[24] The basin was also watered by subterranean aquifers, calling to mind the "springs of the great deep" in 7:11 and 8:2. The correspondence here with Genesis is very striking, but there remains the problem that the author describes one river dividing into four, not four rivers converging into one.[25]

---

[19] See, e.g., Berry, "This Cursed Earth"; Rüst, "Early Humans, Adam, and Inspiration"; Berry and Jeeves, "The Nature of Human Nature"; Alexander, *Creation or Evolution*, Chaps. 9–10.

[20] For further discussion, see my article, "Genesis 1–3 as a Theodicy".

[21] See Rohl, *A Test of Time*, Vol. 2, Chap. 1.

[22] Rose, "New Light on Human Prehistory in the Arabo-Persian Gulf Oasis".

[23] "The Rivers of Paradise", pp. 25–26.

[24] Wenham, *Genesis 1–15*, p. 65.

[25] Driver, *Genesis*, p. 39; Currid, *Genesis*, Vol. 1, p. 102.

Extent of the Curse

Death of animals

Some commentators take Romans 5:12 ("through one human being sin entered the world, and through sin death, and so death spread to all human beings, in that all sinned") to indicate that Adam's sin led to the death of animals as well as of human beings. Others confine the reference to human beings. Either reading is possible — in Romans, "world" (*kosmos*) can refer to the whole created order (as in 1:20) or just to the world of human beings (3:6, 19).

Genesis 5: Adam to Noah

Some scholars think that the numbers in Genesis 5 and 11 are symbolic.[26] This is because most of them end in zero or five, and the remainder can be obtained by adding multiples of seven. However, those ending in zero or five could be rounded, and the remainder could be random.[27]

Genesis 6–9: the Flood

In the text, I compare the ark with the North Sea Ferry, Norstar. This and its sister-ship, the Norland (which went to the Falklands), have now been broken up. Their replacements, the Norsea and the Norsun, now named the Pride of York and the Pride of Bruges, are similar in size. The Pride of Hull and the Pride of Rotterdam are bigger.

Extent of the Flood

The "Great Sea" in the quotation from Philo was almost certainly the Mediterranean, not the Atlantic as suggested by the Loeb translator.

---

[26] Cassuto, *Genesis*, pp. 12–17; Hill, "A Third Alternative to Concordism and Divine Accommodation".

[27] See my note, "Numerology in Genesis". Hill criticizes this ("Response to P.G. Nelson's 'Numerology in Genesis'"), but if the rounded numbers are omitted from the ages she considers, the chances of the remaining numbers ending with the digits they do are only one in 1024 (4^5).

Genesis 10 and 11: Noah to Abraham

In the text, I take Genesis 11:1–9 as explaining the dispersion of Noah's descendants in Genesis 10.[28] Genesis 11:2 then describes the migration of all of Noah's descendants ("all the '*ereṣ*" of 11:1) to the land of Shinar. This reading is supported by references in Genesis 10 that anticipate 11:1–9 — viz. settlement at Babel in Shinar (v. 10) and people having different languages (vv. 5, 20, 31).

An alternative reading is to take 11:2 as describing Noah's descendants travelling south to *extend* the area they occupied. Genesis 10 can then be read before 11:1–9 as describing the dispersal of Noah's descendants and 11:2 as a stage in this process after the Ararat region had been resettled, and "all the '*ereṣ*" still had one language. Genesis 11:1–9 then describes the movement south and confusion of languages. This reading explains why the builders of the tower of Babel were fearful of being attacked, there being other descendants of Noah from where they came.

Chapter 5 Evidence for the Flood

In this chapter, I set out different possibilities for the Flood. I have tried to narrow these down in an article, "Another Look at the Genesis Flood".

5.1 Preliminary considerations

Date

Radiocarbon dating

Recent work has shown that the calibrated dates that were estimated in Table 5.1 are as shown overleaf.[29]

The differences for the earliest dates are considerably higher than estimated in Table 5.1 (1000 years), but this does not greatly affect my conclusions.

---

[28] Cf. Wenham, *Genesis* 1–15, p. 242; Currid, *Genesis*, Vol. 1, p. 238.
[29] http://c14.arch.ox.ac.uk/intcal09.14c

Uncalibrated	Calibrated	Difference
7000 B.C.	8200 B.C.	1200
8000 B.C.	9400 B.C.	1400
9000 B.C.	10,800 B.C.	1800
10,000 B.C.	11,900 B.C.	1900
11,000 B.C.	13,300 B.C.	2300

Date of Flood

Another approach to dating the Flood is to consider the movement of population described in Genesis. As we have seen, the author gives the impression that the first human population lived around Eden, which we have located on the plateau north of Mesopotamia. Then came the Flood, and the grounding of the ark on "the mountains of Ararat" (8:4), in the same general region. After this, Noah's descendants dispersed to become the various nations known to the ancient Hebrews by a process that involved some or all of them travelling south to Mesopotamia (11:2).

Now there is archaeological evidence for the movement of population from the Turkish-Iranian plateau on to the Mesopotamian plain.[30] Archaeologists date this to **6000/5000–4000**/3300 B.C. This dates the Flood to sometime before 6000/5000 B.C., depending on the time taken for Noah's family to build up numbers after the Flood.

Mesopotamian flood stories

Scholars continue to place the Genesis flood in Mesopotamia.[31] Robert Best thinks that "Mount Niṣir" in the Epic of Gilgamesh is a mistranslation, and that the reference is to a sand bank in the Persian Gulf.[32]

---

[30] Barraclough and Parker, *The Times Atlas of World History*, pp. 40–41.
[31] Best, *Noah's Ark and the Ziusudra Epic*; Hill, "A Time and a Place for Noah"; Seely, "Noah's Flood". Cf. Irving Finkel, *The Ark before Noah*, Hodder and Stoughton, London, 2014.
[32] *Noah's Ark and the Ziusudra Epic*, p. 277.

Noah's world

Recalibrated dates for the beginnings of agriculture and metal-working are 9500/**8000** B.C. and 9000/**7500** B.C. respectively. Archaeologists now have evidence that agriculture began around 11,000/**9000** B.C.[33] This means that the Flood could have been considerably earlier than the date suggested in the text (9500/8000 B.C., recalibrated).

A further consideration is that, after the Flood, "Noah, a man of the ground, began and planted a vineyard" (9:20 lit.). This could mean that he was the first person to cultivate vines, a practice for which archaeologists have found evidence on the Turkish-Iranian plateau dating back to about 7000/**6000** B.C.[34] This would date the Flood to sometime *before* this. On the other hand, this verse could mean that the first thing Noah did after the Flood was to plant vines, or that he took up an activity that he had previously eschewed (compare verse 21). In this case, the Flood would have taken place sometime *after* the development of viti-culture.

Paul Seely thinks the Flood took place after the domestication of fruit trees (about **4000**/3300 BC) because of the fruit trees in Genesis 2–3.[35] However, these had been planted by God (2:8–9). Adam's punishment was to eat the plants of the field (3:17–19).

Conclusions

The recalibrated date in (1) is 9500/8000 B.C. As noted above, the Flood could have been considerably earlier than this. The end-date in (2)–(4) could be 6000/5000 B.C. if the dating of the movement of population discussed above is correct.

---

[33] Moore *et al.*, *Village on the Euphrates*, pp. 478, 479.
[34] McGovern *et al*, "The Beginnings of Winemaking and Viniculture in the Ancient Near East and Egypt"; Phillips, *A Short History of Wine*, Chap.1.
[35] Seely, "Noah's Flood", pp. 291–292.

5.2 Evidence for a global flood

Archaeological evidence

Victor Pearce's evidence for a global flood has been overtaken by new discoveries. Recent work has shown that there are no contemporaneous breaks in occupation at Middle Eastern sites back to **12,300**/10,300 B.C.[36]

5.3 Evidence for a flood of Noah's world

Scholars have associated the Genesis flood with the flooding that led to the formation of the Persian Gulf when sea levels rose after the last Ice Age.[37] This flooding was eventually permanent, but there could have been a temporary deluge at an intermediate stage.

5.4 Evidence for a widespread flood

Patrick O'Connell thought the Flood was of the inhabited world.[38] He arrived at a date of 7000 B.C. for this, but by conflating evidence of flooding in the ancient world.[39]

Chapter 6 God's role in creation if the scientific account is correct

Richard Dawkins and Peter Atkins (ref. 1) continue to argue against belief in God.[40] I have presented an alternative line of reasoning for general readers which answers the points they make.[41]

---

[36] Mithen, *After the Ice*, Chaps. 3–11; Seely, 'Noah's Flood,' pp. 301–302.

[37] Olson, "Has Science Dated the Biblical Flood?"; Bailey, *Noah*, pp. 40–45; Teller *et al*, "Calcareous Dunes of the United Arab Emirates and Noah's Flood".

[38] O'Connell, *Science of To-day and the Problems of Genesis*, Book II, Part I.

[39] On his explanation of the salt desert ("Great Kavir") on the Iranian plateau (pp. 57–59), compare Ganji, "Post-Glacial Climatic Changes on the Iranian Plateau".

[40] Dawkins, *The God Delusion* and other books; Atkins, *On Being*.

[41] Nelson, *The Logic of Life*.

6.2 God's role

To reference 8, add Davies, *The Goldilocks Enigma/The Cosmic Jackpot*. To references 12 and 13, add Hawking and Mlodinow, *The Grand Design*. The "many worlds" interpretation of the quantum theory referred to in note 14 has now been discredited.[42]

Chapter 7 Interpreting Genesis

7.2 Use of figurative language in the Bible

Simplification

A popular idea today is that, to make Genesis intelligible to its first readers, its author employed the ideas his contemporaries had about the material world, whether right or wrong.[43] Thus, for example, Genesis follows the *Enûma eliš* (Box 3.1, p. 36) in starting from water, there being a division to form the earth and the sky, the creation next of the sun, moon, and stars, and the creation lastly of human beings.

An obvious problem with this proposal is that the author of Genesis did not need to adopt the ideas of his contemporaries to the extent that is suggested. For example, if his contemporaries were mistaken about the order of creation, he could still present the order correctly without making it unintelligible. There is not, in any case, exact correspondence between Genesis and the *Enûma eliš* — the latter starts with two kinds of water, and refers to a long interval of time (Tablet I, line 13).[44]

---

[42] McWeeny, "Quantum Chemistry", pp. 26–29.
[43] See, e.g., Walton, *The Lost World of Genesis One*; Tinker, *Reclaiming Genesis*; Carlson and Longman, *Science, Creation and the Bible*.
[44] Pritchard (ed.), *Ancient Near Eastern Texts*, p. 61, n. 6.

Chapter 8 Harmonization of accounts (method 1)

8.1 Theology of Genesis

On the effects of the Curse, see further my article, "Genesis 1–3 as a Theodicy". Alternative theodicies (ref. 5) include John Polkinghorne's idea that God has given the natural world freedom to evolve as it will just as he has given human beings freedom to live as they choose.[45]

Christians need a robust theodicy, both to support them in their own belief and to help them to commend their belief to others. Many people find suffering a serious obstacle to belief.[46]

When Jesus was asked about a massacre of Galileans by Pilate's soldiers in the temple in Jerusalem, he said (Luke 13:1–5):

> "Do you think that these Galileans were worse sinners than all the other Galileans because they suffered these things? I tell you, no. But unless you repent, you will all likewise perish. Or those eighteen on whom [as a result of an earth tremor?] the tower in Siloam fell and killed them, do you think that they were worse short-comers than all the others living in Jerusalem? I tell you, no. But unless you repent, you will all similarly perish."

Here Jesus counters the idea that a disaster is necessarily due to the particular sins of the people concerned, but nevertheless links such disasters to sin — the sin of humanity generally. He thus treats them as having their origin in the Curse.

Thankfully, Jesus goes on to teach that God is patient, and gives everyone time and encouragement to repent (vv. 6–9).

[45] See, e.g., Polkinghorne, *Science and Providence*, Chap. 5.
[46] See, e.g., Humphreys, *In God We Doubt*.

8.2 Harmonization

The Fall and the Curse

Compare William Dembski's treatment in his recent book, *The End of Christianity: Finding a Good God in an Evil World*.

Free will

I develop approach (4), and extend my discussion of other approaches, in my article, "Free Will in a Deterministic Universe". This includes a consideration of Nancey Murphy's "nonreductive physicalism"[47] and of William Hasker's "emergent dualism".[48]

Chapter 9 Assumptions in scientific account

9.2 Fixity of natural law and complete conformity to it

I refer to BBC Radio 4's "UK Theme". This is a medley of tunes from different parts of the United Kingdom ending with "Pomp and Circumstance". It used to be played at the beginning of Radio 4 each day.

Chapter 10 Harmonization of accounts (method 2)

10.1 Outline

Note that this method of reconciling Genesis and modern science satisfies the requirement that we imposed on the first method that scientific developments should not pre-empt faith (Chap. 7). We can never *prove*

---

[47] Murphy, 'Nonreductive Physicalism".
[48] Hasker, *The Emergent Self*.

that God created the universe in the way that Genesis describes, only believe that he did.

10.2 Details

Adam and Eve

This section is complicated by the different possibilities. Here I consider the simplest case in more detail.

If Genesis is taken literally, God created Adam and Eve supernaturally in a pre-Cursed state — eating only vegetables (1:29) and made to be immortal (2:8–9, 16–17). The earth was also in a pre-Cursed state, with no human remains on it.

What happened at the Curse depends on the scientific picture. The simplest case is if, in the post-Curse world scientists study, modern humans have a single origin, and Adam and Eve were the first pair. This dates them well before the genealogical date (currently to 200,000–150,000 B.P.) implying that the genealogies are incomplete. This can be explained by the need to ensure that acceptance of Genesis is always a matter of faith. If the scientific date and genealogical date coincided, it would make acceptance a matter of sight.

In this simple case, what happens at the Curse is that Adam and Eve are changed (they become mortal) and the earth is changed with them. In this changed state, if science is right, Adam and Eve become part of a natural order that, if it had been in this state before the Curse, would have evolved to produce them. The changed earth bears the marks of this evolution in the form of the fossil record and associated artefacts. But this evolution did not actually take place; it rather reflects the current design of the universe, and what would have taken place if the universe had always had this design.

A further question is: what were in Adam and Eve's minds when they were created? As they were mature human beings, one would expect them to have memories, yet they did not have histories (childhood, adolescence, etc.) to remember. God must therefore have told them how he had created them, as described in Genesis 2.[49] Thus Adam knew that God had made Eve out of his rib ("... she shall be called 'woman' because she was taken out of man", 2:23), and that he himself had been made out of dust, as God reminded him after his fall ("dust you are, and to dust you shall return", 3:19). God must also have created the couple with a knowledge of how to live, e.g. how to grow food (2:15, 3:17–19).

Pre-Adamite human remains

This section is also complicated by the different possibilities. In the simple case I have just discussed, "pre-Adamites" are *Homo* species scientists believe evolved into modern humans. "Non-Adamites" are other *Homo* species.

10.3 Scientific status

I discuss the idea of a mature creation further, and answer objections to it, in my article, "Another Look at Mature Creation".

Chapter 11 Conclusions

11.3 Tolerance

Compare the even-handed approach taken by Rau in *Mapping the Origins Debate*.

---

[49] Cf. Poythress, *Redeeming Science*, p. 117. While preferring to take the "days" as analogical and long (Chap. 10), he makes a good case for mature creation (Chap. 9).

Bibliography

Adams, Marilyn McCord, and Adams, Robert Merrihew (eds.), *The Problem of Evil*, Oxford University Press, 1990.

Ager, Derek V., *The Nature of the Stratigraphical Record*, 3rd edn., Wiley, Chichester, 1993.

Ager, Derek, *The New Catastrophism*, Cambridge University Press, 1993.

Aitken, M.J., *Science-based Dating in Archaeology*, Longman, London, 1990.

Albright, W.F., *New Horizons in Biblical Research*, Oxford University Press, 1966.

Andrews, E.H., *Is Evolution Scientific?*, Evangelical Press, Welwyn, 1977.

Andrews, E.H., *From Nothing to Nature*, Evangelical Press, Welwyn, 1978.

Andrews, E.H., *God, Science and Evolution*, Evangelical Press, Welwyn, 1980.

Andrews, E.H., "The Age of the Earth", in *Creation and Evolution* (ed. Burke, Derek), Inter-Varsity Press, Leicester, 1985.

Andrews, E.H., *Christ and the Cosmos*, Evangelical Press, Welwyn, 1986.

Andrews, Peter, and Stringer, Christopher, "The Primates' Progress", in *The Book of Life* (ed. Gould, Stephen Jay), Norton, New York, 1993.

Atkins, P.W., *The Creation*, Freeman, Oxford, 1981; revised edn., *Creation Revisited*, 1992.

Augros, Robert, and Stanciu, George, *The New Biology*, Shambhala, Boston, 1987.

Austin, Steven A., "Did Noah's Flood Cover the Entire World? — Yes", in *The Genesis Debate* (ed. Youngblood, Ronald F.), Nelson, Nashville, 1986; Baker, Grand Rapids, 1990.

Ball, C.J., *Light from the East*, Eyre and Spottiswoode, London, 1899.

Barraclough, Geoffrey, and Parker, Geoffrey, *The Times Atlas of World History*, 4th edn., Times Books, London, 1993.

Barrow, John D., and Silk, Joseph, *The Left Hand of Creation: The Origin and Evolution of the Expanding Universe*, 2nd edn., Oxford University Press, 1993.

Barrow, John D., and Tipler, Frank J., *The Anthropic Cosmological Principle*, Oxford University Press, 1986.

Behe, Michael J., *Darwin's Black Box: The Biochemical Challenge to Evolution*, Free Press, New York, 1996.

Berg, Paul, and Singer, Maxine, *Dealing with Genes: The Language of Heredity*, University Science Books, Mill Valley, California, 1992.

Berry, R.J., *God and Evolution*, Hodder and Stoughton, London, 1988.

Berry, R.J., *God and the Biologist*, Apollos, Leicester, 1996.

Birkett, Kirsten, *Unnatural Enemies: An Introduction to Science and Christianity*, Matthias Media, Sydney, 1997.

Bloch, Salman, "Some Factors Controlling the Concentration of Uranium in the World Ocean", *Geochimica et Cosmochimica Acta*, Vol. 44, 1980, pp. 373–377.

Blocher, Henri, *In the Beginning* (tr. Preston, David G.), Inter-Varsity Press, Leicester, 1984.

Boardman, Donald C., "Did Noah's Flood Cover the Entire World? — No", in *The Genesis Debate* (ed. Youngblood, Ronald F.), Nelson, Nashville, 1986; Baker, Grand Rapids, 1990.

Bowden, Malcolm, *Ape-men — Fact or Fallacy?*, Sovereign Publications, Bromley, Kent, 2nd edn., 1981.

Bowden, Malcolm, *The Rise of the Evolution Fraud*, Sovereign Publications, Bromley, Kent, 1982.

Bowden, Malcolm, *Science vs Evolution*, Sovereign Publications, Bromley, Kent, 1991.

Bowden, Malcolm, *True Science Agrees with the Bible*, Sovereign Publications, Bromley, Kent, 1998.

Brand, Leonard, *Faith, Reason, and Earth History*, Andrews University Press, Berrien Springs, Michigan, 1997.

Brice, William C. (ed.), *The Environmental History of the Near and Middle East since the Last Ice Age*, Academic Press, London, 1978.

Brinkmann, R., *Geology of Turkey*, Elsevier, Amsterdam, 1976.

Brown, Walter T., *In the Beginning: Compelling Evidence for Creation and the Flood*, Center for Scientific Creation, Phoenix, 6th edn., 1995.

Brown, Warren S.; Murphy, Nancey; and Malony, H. Newton (eds.), *Whatever Happened to the Soul?*, Fortress Press, Minneapolis, 1998.

Bryce, James, *Transcaucasia and Ararat*, Macmillan, London, 1877.

Burke, Derek C. (ed.), *Creation and Evolution*, Inter-Varsity Press, Leicester, 1985.

Cameron, Nigel M. de S., *Evolution and the Authority of the Bible*, Paternoster, Exeter, 1983.

Cansdale, George, *Animals of Bible Lands*, Paternoster, Exeter, 1970.

Cassuto, U., *A Commentary on the Book of Genesis* (tr. Abrahams, Israel), Magnes Press, Jerusalem, Vol. 1, 1961; Vol. 2, 1964.

Chateaubriand, François-Auguste, *Génie du Christianisme*, Migneret, Paris, 1802.

Clark, W.E. Le Gros, *The Fossil Evidence for Human Evolution*, 3rd edn. (revised by Campbell, Bernard G.), University of Chicago Press, 1978.

Cohen, Jack, and Stewart, Ian, *The Collapse of Chaos: Discovering Simplicity in a Complex World*, Viking, London, 1994.

Coles, Peter, "The End of the Old Model Universe", *Nature*, Vol. 393, 1998, pp. 741–744.

Collyer, John V., *Creation, Evolution and Science*, The Testimony, Norwich, 1993.

Cooper, Bill, *After the Flood: The Early Post-Flood History of Europe*, New Wine Press, Chichester, 1995.

Corey, M.A., *Back to Darwin: The Scientific Case for Deistic Evolution*, University Press of America, Lanham, Maryland, 1994.

Cornwall, Ian, *Ice Ages: Their Nature and Effects*, John Baker, London/Humanities Press, New York, 1970.

Craig, Edward (ed.), *Routledge Encyclopedia of Philosophy* (in 10 vols.), Routledge, London, 1998.

Crick, Francis, *Life Itself: Its Origin and Nature*, Macdonald, London, 1982.

Crick, Francis, *The Astonishing Hypothesis: The Scientific Search for the Soul*, Simon and Schuster, London, 1994.

Croft, L.R., *Handbook of Protein Sequences*, Joynson-Bruvvers Ltd., Oxford, 1973.

Croft, L.R., *How Life Began*, Evangelical Press, Darlington, 1988.

Crompton, A.W., and Jenkins, Farish A., Jr., "Origin of Mammals", in *Mesozoic Mammals* (ed. Lillegraven, Jason A.; Kielan-Jaworowska, Zofia; and Clemens, William A.), University of California Press, Berkeley, 1979 (Chap. 3).

Custance, Arthur C., "Flood Traditions of the World", in *Symposium on Creation IV* (ed. Patten, Donald W.), Baker, Grand Rapids, 1972.

Darwin, Charles, *The Origin of Species* [Full title: *On the Origin of Species by Means of Natural Selection, or the Preservation of Favoured Races in the Struggle for Life*], John Murray, London, 1859.

Davies, P.C.W., *The Accidental Universe*, Cambridge University Press, 1982.

Davies, Paul, *God and the New Physics*, Dent, London, 1983.

Davies, Paul C.W., *The Cosmic Blueprint*, Heinemann, London, 1987.

Davies, Paul C.W., *The Mind of God: Science and the Search for Ultimate Meaning*, Simon and Schuster, London, 1992.

Davies, P.C.W., and Brown, J.R. (eds.), *The Ghost in the Atom*, Cambridge University Press, 1986.

Dawkins, Richard, *The Selfish Gene*, Oxford University Press, 1976.

Dawkins, Richard, *The Blind Watchmaker*, Longman, Harlow, 1986.

Dawkins, Richard, *River out of Eden: A Darwinian View of Life*, Weidenfeld and Nicolson, London, 1995.

Dawkins, Richard, *Climbing Mount Improbable*, Viking, London, 1996.

Dawkins, Richard, *Unweaving the Rainbow*, Penguin, London, 1998.

Dayhoff, Margaret O. (ed.), *Atlas of Protein Sequence and Structure*, Vol. 5, National Biomedical Research Foundation, Washington, 1972.

de Duve, Christian, *Vital Dust: Life as a Cosmic Imperative*, BasicBooks, New York, 1995.

Delsemme, Armand, *Our Cosmic Origins: From the Big Bang to the Emergence of Life and Intelligence*, Cambridge University Press, 1998.

Denbigh, K.G., and Denbigh, J.S., *Entropy in Relation to Incomplete Knowledge*, Cambridge University Press, 1985.

Denness, Bruce, "Divine Artefact", *Nature*, Vol. 336, 1988, p. 614.

Denton, Michael, *Evolution: A Theory in Crisis*, Burnett, London, 1985.

Denton, Michael J., *Nature's Destiny: How the Laws of Biology Reveal Purpose in the Universe*, Free Press, New York, 1998.

Deutsch, Alexander, and 12 others, "The Impact–Flood Connection: Does It Exist?", *Terra Nova*, Vol. 6, 1994, pp. 644-650.

Deutsch, David, *The Fabric of Reality*, Penguin, London, 1997.

Diamond, Jared, "Location, Location, Location: The First Farmers", *Science*, Vol. 278, 1997, pp. 1243-1244.

Driver, S.R., *Hebrew Tenses* [Full title: *A Treatise on the Use of the Tenses in Hebrew*], Oxford University Press, 3rd edn., 1892.

Driver, S.R., *Genesis* [Full title: *The Book of Genesis*], Westminster Commentaries, Methuen, London, 14th edn., 1943.

Eddington, A.S., *The Nature of the Physical World*, Cambridge University Press, 1928.

Eicher, Don L., *Geologic Time*, Prentice-Hall, Englewood Cliffs, 2nd edn., 1976.

Eldredge, Niles, *Reinventing Darwin*, Wiley, New York, 1995.

Eldredge, Niles, and Gould, Stephen Jay, "Punctuated Equilibria: An Alternative to Phyletic Gradualism", in *Models in Paleobiology* (ed. Schopf, Thomas J.M.), Freeman, Cooper and Co., San Francisco, 1972.

Ferguson, Kitty, *The Fire in the Equations*, Bantam, London, 1994.

Fergusson, David A.S., *The Cosmos and the Creator: An Introduction to the Theology of Creation*, SPCK, London, 1998.

Ferrière, Régis, "Help and You Shall Be Helped", *Nature*, Vol. 393, 1998, pp. 517-519.

Fischer, Dick, *The Origins Solution*, Fairway Press, Lima, Ohio, 1996.

Forster, Roger, and Marston, Paul, *Christianity, Evidence and Truth*, Monarch, Crowborough, 1995.

Fraser, A.G., "The Age of the Earth", in *Creation and Evolution* (ed. Burke, Derek), Inter-Varsity Press, Leicester, 1985.

Frazer, Sir James George, *Folk-lore in the Old Testament* (in 3 vols.), Macmillan, London, 1918.

Gibbons, Ann, "A New Face for Human Ancestors", *Science*, Vol. 276, 1997, pp. 1331-1333.

Gish, Duane T., *Evolution: The Fossils Say No!*, Creation-Life, San Diego, California, 2nd edn., 1973.

Gish, Duane T., *Evolution: The Challenge of the Fossil Record*, Creation-Life, El Cajon, California, 1985.

Gleick, James, *Chaos*, Viking, New York, 1987.

Goldberg, Edward D., "The Processes Regulating the Composition of Sea Water", *Journal of Chemical Education*, Vol. 35, 1958, pp. 116–119.

Goldschmidt, Richard, *The Material Basis of Evolution*, Yale University Press, New Haven, 1940.

Goodwin, Brian, *How the Leopard Changed Its Spots: The Evolution of Complexity*, Weidenfeld and Nicolson, London, 1994.

Gosse, Philip Henry, *Omphalos: An Attempt to Untie the Geological Knot*, van Voorst, London, 1857.

Gribbin, John, and Rees, Martin, *The Stuff of the Universe*, Heinemann, London, 1990; republished as *Cosmic Coincidences*, Black Swan, London, 1991.

Hajdas, Irena; Ivy-Ochs, Susan D.; and Bonani, Georges, "Problems in the Extension of the Radiocarbon Calibration Curve (10–13 kyr BP)", *Radiocarbon*, Vol. 37, 1995, pp. 75–79.

Hall, Nina (ed.), *The New Scientist Guide to Chaos*, Penguin, London, 1992.

Hamilton, Victor P., *Genesis 1–17* [Full title: *The Book of Genesis Chapters 1–17*], New International Commentary on the Old Testament, Eerdmans, Grand Rapids, 1990.

Hawking, Stephen W., *A Brief History of Time*, Bantam, London, 1988.

Hayward, Alan, *Creation and Evolution*, 1st edn., SPCK, London, 1985; 2nd edn., Bethany House, Minneapolis, 1995.

Hedges, R.E.M., "Dated Theory in a Flux?", *Education in Chemistry*, Vol. 35, 1998, p. 39.

Heidel, Alexander, *The Babylonian Genesis*, University of Chicago Press, 2nd edn., 1951.

Heun, Manfred; Schäfer-Pregl, Ralf; Klawan, Dieter; Castagna, Renato; Accerbi, Monica; Borghi, Basilio; and Salamini, Francesco, "Site of Einkorn Wheat Domestication Identified by DNA Fingerprinting", *Science*, Vol. 278, 1997, pp. 1312–1314.

Holder, Rodney D., *Nothing but Atoms and Molecules?: Probing the Limits of Science*, Monarch, Tunbridge Wells, 1993.

Hooke, S.H., *In the Beginning*, Oxford University Press, 1947.

Hoyle, Fred, and Wickramasinghe, Chandra, *Lifecloud: The Origin of Life in the Universe*, Dent, London, 1978.

Hoyle, Fred, and Wickramasinghe, Chandra, *Evolution from Space*, Dent, London, 1981.

Hoyle, Fred, and Wickramasinghe, Chandra, *Our Place in the Cosmos*, Dent, London, 1993.

Humphreys, D. Russell, *Starlight and Time: Solving the Puzzle of Distant Starlight in a Young Universe*, Master Books, Colorado Springs, 1995.

Hunten, Donald M., "Escape of Atmospheres, Ancient and Modern", *Icarus*, Vol. 85, 1990, pp. 1–20.

Jantsch, Erich, *The Self-organizing Universe*, Pergamon, Oxford, 1980.

Jeeves, Malcolm, *Mind Fields: Reflections on the Science of Mind and Brain*, Lancer, Homebush West, Australia/Apollos, Leicester, 1994.

Jeeves, Malcolm A., *Human Nature at the Millennium: Reflections on the Integration of Psychology and Christianity*, Baker, Grand Rapids/Apollos, Leicester, 1997.

Jeeves, Malcolm A., and Berry, R.J., *Science, Life and Christian Belief*, Apollos, Leicester, 1998.

Johnson, Michael R., *Genesis, Geology and Catastrophism: A Critique of Creationist Science and Biblical Literalism*, Paternoster, Exeter, 1988.

Johnson, Phillip E., *Darwin on Trial*, InterVarsity Press, Downers Grove, Illinois, 1st edn., 1991; 2nd edn., 1993.

Johnson, Phillip E., *Defeating Darwinism*, InterVarsity Press, Downers Grove, Illinois, 1997; *Testing Darwinism*, IVP, Leicester, 1997.

Jones, Steve, "Why a Big Bang is Best Evidence of an Open Mind", *The Daily Telegraph*, 13 September 1995, p. 14.

Jones, Steve; Martin, Robert; and Pilbeam, David (eds.), *The Cambridge Encyclopedia of Human Evolution*, Cambridge University Press, 1992.

Kauffman, Stuart A., *The Origins of Order: Self-Organization and Selection in Evolution*, Oxford University Press, 1993.

Kauffman, Stuart A., *At Home in the Universe: The Search for Laws of Self-Organization and Complexity*, Oxford University Press, 1995; Viking, London, 1995.

Kelly, Douglas F., *Creation and Change: Genesis 1.1–2.4 in the Light of Changing Scientific Paradigms*, Mentor, Fearn, Ross-shire, 1997.

Kemp, T.S., *Mammal-like Reptiles and the Origin of Mammals*, Academic Press, London, 1982.

Kenyon, Dean H., and Steinman, Gary, *Biochemical Predestination*, McGraw-Hill, New York, 1969.

Kerkut, G.A., *Implications of Evolution*, Pergamon, Oxford, 1960.

Kerr, Richard A., "Pushing Back the Origins of Animals", *Science*, Vol. 279, 1998, pp. 803–804.

Kerr, Richard A., "Black Sea Deluge May Have Helped Spread Farming", *Science*, Vol. 279, 1998, p. 1132.

Kidner, Derek, *Genesis*, Tyndale, London, 1967.

Kitchen, K.A., *Ancient Orient and Old Testament*, Tyndale, London, 1966.

Kline, Meredith G., "Genesis", in *The New Bible Commentary: Revised* (eds. Guthrie, D.; Motyer, J.A.; Stibbs, A.M.; and Wiseman, D.J.), Inter-Varsity Press, London, 1970.

Kramer, Samuel Noah, "Reflections on the Mesopotamian Flood: The Cuneiform Data New and Old", *Expedition*, Summer 1967, pp. 12–18.

Krings, Matthias; Stone, Anne; Schmitz, Ralf W.; Krainitzki, Heike; Stoneking, Mark; and Pääbo, Svante, "Neandertal DNA Sequences and the Origin of Modern Humans", *Cell*, Vol. 90, 1997, pp. 19–30.

Kristan-Tollmann, Edith, and Tollmann, Alexander, "The Youngest Big Impact on Earth Deduced from Geological and Historical Evidence", *Terra Nova*, Vol. 6, 1994, pp. 209–217.

Kristan-Tollmann, Edith, and Tollmann, Alexander, "Reply to a Reply — But the Flood Really Happened!", *Terra Nova*, Vol. 8, 1996, 108.

Lang, Bernhard, "Non-Semitic Deluge Stories and the Book of Genesis: A Bibliographical and Critical Survey", *Anthropos*, Vol. 80, 1985, pp. 605–616.

Layzer, David, *Cosmogenesis*, Oxford University Press, 1990.

Lerner, Eric J., *The Big Bang Never Happened*, Times Books, New York, 1991.

Leslie, John, *Universes*, Routledge, London, 1989.

Lester, Lane P., and Bohlin, Raymond G., *The Natural Limits to Biological Change*, Zondervan, Grand Rapids, 1984.

Libes, Susan M., *An Introduction to Marine Biogeochemistry*, Wiley, New York, 1992.

Lovelock, J.E., *Gaia: A New Look at Life on Earth*, Oxford University Press, 1979.

Løvtrup, Søren, *Darwinism: The Refutation of a Myth*, Croom Helm, London, 1987.

Lucas, Ernest, *Genesis Today*, Scripture Union, London, 1989.

Lynch, John, *Life is Impossible*, BBC, London, 1993.

MacKay, Donald M., *Freedom of Action in a Mechanistic Universe*, Cambridge University Press, 1967.

MacKay, Donald M., "The Sovereignty of God in the Natural World", *Scottish Journal of Theology*, Vol. 21, 1968, pp. 13–26. (Reproduced in *The Open Mind and Other Essays*.)

MacKay, Donald M., *The Clockwork Image: A Christian Perspective on Science*, Inter-Varsity Press, London, 1974.

MacKay, Donald M., *Science, Chance, and Providence*, Oxford University Press, 1978.

MacKay, Donald M., *The Open Mind and Other Essays* (ed. Tinker, Melvin), Inter-Varsity Press, Leicester, 1988.

Mackay, Donald M., *Behind the Eye*, Blackwell, Oxford, 1991.

Maddox, John (ed.), "Frontiers of Ignorance", *Nature*, Vol. 372, 1994, pp. 11–36.

Mallowan, M.E.L., "Noah's Flood Reconsidered", *Iraq*, Vol. 26, 1964, pp. 62–82.

Marston, Paul, and Forster, Roger, *Reason and Faith*, Monarch, Eastbourne, 1989.

Maynard Smith, John, *The Problems of Biology*, Oxford University Press, 1986.

McIntosh, Andy, *Genesis for Today: Showing the Relevance of the Creation/Evolution Debate to Today's Society*, Day One, Epsom, 1997.

McMenamin, Mark, *The Garden of Ediacara*, Columbia University Press, 1998.

Mellaart, James, *The Neolithic of the Near East*, Thames and Hudson, London, 1975.

Midgley, Mary, *Evolution as a Religion*, Methuen, London, 1985.

Milton, Richard, *The Facts of Life: Shattering the Myth of Darwinism*, Fourth Estate, London, 1992.

Monod, Jacques, *Chance and Necessity* (tr. Wainhouse, Austryn), Collins, London, 1972.

Moreland, J.P. (ed.), *The Creation Hypothesis*, InterVarsity Press, Downers Grove, Illinois, 1994.

Morris, Henry M. (ed.), *Scientific Creationism*, 1st edn., Creation-Life, San Diego, California, 1974; 2nd edn., Master Books, El Cajon, California, 1985.

Morris, Henry M., *Biblical Creationism*, Baker Books, Grand Rapids, 1993.

Morris, Henry M., and Parker, Gary E., *What Is Creation Science?*, 2nd edn., Master Books, El Cajon, California, 1987.

Morris, J.D., *The Young Earth*, Master Books, Colorado Springs, 1994.

Muir, Ramsay, and Philip, George (eds.), *Philips' Atlas of Ancient and Classical History*, Philip, London, 1938.

Narlikar, Jayant V., *The Primeval Universe*, Oxford University Press 1988.

Nelson, Peter G., *God's Control over the Universe*, Whittles Publishing, Latheronwheel, Caithness, 1992.

Nelson, P.G., *What is the Gospel?*, Whittles Publishing, Latheronwheel, Caithness, 1997.

Newman, Robert C., and Eckelmann, Herman J., Jr., *Genesis One and the Origin of the Earth*, InterVarsity Press, Downers Grove, Illinois, 1977.

Nicolis, Grégoire, and Prigogine, Ilya, *Exploring Complexity*, Freeman, New York, 1989.

Norman, Trevor, and Setterfield, Barry, "The Atomic Constants, Light, and Time", Invited Research Report, Stanford Research Institute International, Menlo Park, California, 1987.

Nowak, Martin A., and Sigmund, Karl, "Evolution of Indirect Reciprocity by Image Scoring", *Nature*, Vol. 393, 1998, pp. 573–577.

Nützel, Werner, "The Climate Changes of Mesopotamia and Bordering Areas: 14000 to 2000 B.C.", *Sumer*, Vol. 32, 1976, pp. 11–24.

O'Connell, Patrick, *Science of Today and the Problems of Genesis: the Six Days of Creation, the Origin of Man, the Deluge and the Antiquity of Man: A Vindication of the Papal Encyclicals and Rulings of the Church on These Questions* (in 2 vols.), Radio Replies Press Society, Minnesota, 1959.

Parrot, André, *The Flood and Noah's Ark* (tr. Hudson, Edwin), SCM Press, London, 1955.

Peacocke, A.R., *Creation and the World of Science*, Oxford University Press, 1979.

Peacocke, Arthur, *God and the New Biology*, Dent, London, 1986.

Peacocke, Arthur, *Theology for a Scientific Age*, 1st edn., Blackwell, Oxford, 1990; 2nd, enlarged edn., SCM Press, London, 1993.

Pearce, E.K. Victor, *Who Was Adam?*, 2nd edn., Paternoster, Exeter, 1976; 3rd edn., Africa Centre for World Mission, Walkerville, South Africa, 1987.

Pearce, E.K. Victor, *Evidence for Truth* (in 3 vols.), Evidence Programmes, Eastbourne, 1993.

Pearce, E.K. Victor, *Weighing the Evidence*, Alpha, Amersham-on-the-Hill, Bucks, 1993.

Peet, J.H. John, *In the Beginning, GOD Created...*, Grace Publications, London, 1994.

Penn, Granville, *A Comparative Estimate of the Mineral and Mosaical Geologies*, Ogle, Duncan, and Co., London, 1822.

Polkinghorne, John, *One World*, SPCK, London, 1986.

Polkinghorne, John, *Science and Creation*, SPCK, London, 1988.

Polkinghorne, John, *Science and Providence*, SPCK, London, 1989.

Polkinghorne, John, *Reason and Reality*, SPCK, London, 1991.

Polkinghorne, John, *Quarks, Chaos, and Christianity*, Triangle, London, 1994.

Polkinghorne, John, *Serious Talk: Science and Religion in Dialogue*, SCM, London, 1996.

Polkinghorne, John, *Science and Theology*, SPCK, London, 1998.

Polkinghorne, John C., *Belief in God in an Age of Science*, Yale University Press, New Haven, 1998.

Post, G.E., "Dove", "Raven", in *A Dictionary of the Bible* (ed. Hastings, James), T. and T. Clark, Edinburgh, 1898–1904 (Vol. 1, pp. 619–620; Vol. 4, pp. 201–202).

Press, Frank, and Siever, Raymond, *Earth*, Freeman, New York, 4th edn., 1986.

Press, Frank, and Siever, Raymond, *Understanding Earth*, Freeman, New York, 2nd edn., 1997.

Prigogine, Ilya, and Stengers, Isabelle, *Order out of Chaos*, Bantam, Toronto, 1984.

Pritchard, James B. (ed.), *Ancient Near Eastern Texts*, Princeton University Press, 2nd edn., 1955.

Quirke, Stephen, and Spencer, Jeffrey (eds.), *The British Museum Book of Ancient Egypt*, British Museum Press, London, 1992.

Ramm, Bernard, *The Christian View of Science and Scripture*, Paternoster, Exeter, 1955.

Rattray Taylor, Gordon, *The Great Evolution Mystery*, Secker and Warburg, London, 1983.

Ratzsch, Del, *The Battle of Beginnings*, InterVarsity Press, Downers Grove, Illinois, 1996.

Reader, John, *Missing Links: The Hunt for Earliest Man*, Collins, London, 1981.

Rendle Short, A., *Modern Discovery and the Bible*, Inter-Varsity Fellowship, London, 1942.

Rendle-Short, John, *Green Eye of the Storm: Controversy between Science and Christianity in the Lives of Arthur Rendle Short (1880–1953), Philip Henry Gosse (1810–1888), George John Romanes (1848–1894), and the Author*, Banner of Truth, Edinburgh, 1998.

Ridley, Mark, *The Problems of Evolution*, Oxford University Press, 1985.

Ridley, Mark, *Evolution*, Blackwell, Cambridge, Massachusetts, 2nd edn., 1996.

Rohl, David M., *A Test of Time*, Vol. 1, *The Bible: From Myth to History*, Century, London, 1995; Vol. 2, *Legend: The Genesis of Civilisation*, 1998.

Rose, Steven; Lewontin, R.C.; and Kamin, Leon J., *Not in Our Genes: Biology, Ideology and Human Nature*, Pantheon, New York, 1984.

Rosevear, David, *Creation Science*, New Wine Press, Chichester, 1991.

Ruelle, David, *Chance and Chaos*, Princeton University Press, 1991; Penguin, London, 1993.

Ruse, Michael, *Evolutionary Naturalism*, Routledge, London, 1995.

Sailhamer, John H., *Genesis Unbound*, Multnomah Books, Sisters, Oregon, 1996.

Schaeffer, Francis A., *Genesis in Space and Time: The Flow of Biblical History*, Inter-Varsity Press, Illinois, 1972; Hodder and Stoughton, London, 1973.

Schaeffer, Francis A., *No Final Conflict*, Hodder and Stoughton, London, 1975.

Schick, Asher P., and Lekach, Judith, "A High Magnitude Flood in the Sinai Desert", in *Catastrophic Flooding* (eds. Mayer, L., and Nash, D.), Allen and Unwin, Boston, 1987.

Schroeder, Gerald L., *Genesis and the Big Bang*, Bantam, New York, 1990.

Scott, Andrew, *The Creation of Life: Past, Future, Alien*, Blackwell, Oxford, 1986.

Shapiro, Herman S., "Deoxyribonucleic Acid Content Per Cell of Various Organisms", in *Handbook of Biochemistry*, 2nd edn. (ed. Sober, Herbert A.), The Chemical Rubber Co., Cleveland, Ohio, 1970 (pp. H-104 to H-116).

Shapiro, Robert, *Origins: A Skeptic's Guide to the Creation of Life on Earth*, Heinemann, London, 1986.

Silk, Joseph, *The Big Bang*, Freeman, New York, 2nd edn., 1989.

Silk, Joseph, *A Short History of the Universe*, Scientific American Library, New York, 1994; updated, paperback edn., 1997.

Skinner, John, *Genesis* [Full title: *A Critical and Exegetical Commentary on Genesis*], International Critical Commentary, T. and T. Clark, Edinburgh, 2nd edn., 1930.

Smolin, Lee, *The Life of the Cosmos*, Weidenfeld and Nicolson, London, 1997.

Spanner, Douglas C., *Biblical Creation and the Theory of Evolution*, Paternoster, Exeter, 1987.

Stannard, Russell, *Science and Wonders*, Faber and Faber, London, 1996.

Stansfield, William D., *The Science of Evolution*, Macmillan, New York, 1977.

Strickberger, Monroe W., *Genetics*, Macmillan, New York, 3rd edn., 1985.

Stringer, Chris, and McKie, Robin, *African Exodus: The Origins of Modern Humanity*, Jonathan Cape, London, 1996.

Sunderland, Luther D., *Darwin's Enigma: Fossils and Other Problems*, Master, Santee, California, 4th edn., 1988.

Tipler, Frank J., *The Physics of Immortality*, Doubleday, New York, 1994.

Troitskii, V.S., "Physical Constants and Evolution of the Universe", *Astrophysics and Space Science*, Vol. 139, 1987, pp. 389–411.

Tryon, Edward P., "Is the Universe a Vacuum Fluctuation?", *Nature*, Vol. 246, 1973, pp. 396–397.

Tsumura, David Toshio, *The Earth and the Waters in Genesis 1 and 2*, JSOT Press, Sheffield, 1989.

Van Till, Howard J.; Snow, Robert E.; Stek, John H.; and Young, Davis A., *Portraits of Creation: Biblical and Scientific Perspectives on the World's Formation*, Eerdmans, Grand Rapids, 1990.

Van Till, Howard J.; Young, Davis A.; Menninga, Clarence, *Science Held Hostage: What's Wrong with Creation Science AND Evolutionism*, InterVarsity Press, Downers Grove, Illinois, 1988.

Vardy, Peter, *The Puzzle of Evil*, Fount, London, 1992.

Vitaliano, Dorothy B., *Legends of the Earth: Their Geologic Origins*, Indiana University Press, Bloomington, 1973.

Waddle, Diane M., "Matrix Correlation Tests Support a Single Origin for Modern Humans", *Nature*, Vol. 368, 1994, pp. 452–454.

Ward, Keith, *God, Chance and Necessity*, Oneworld, Oxford, 1996.

Ward, Keith, *God, Faith and the New Millennium*, Oneworld, Oxford, 1998.

Weinberg, Steven, *The First Three Minutes*, new edn., Flamingo, London, 1993.

Weinberg, Steven, *Dreams of a Final Theory*, Hutchinson Radius, London, 1993.

Weinberg, Steven, and others, "Life in the Universe", *Scientific American*, Vol. 271, Special Issue, October 1994.

Wenham, Gordon J., *Genesis 1–15*, Word Biblical Commentary Vol. 1, Word Books, Waco, Texas, 1987.

Westermann, Claus, *Genesis 1–11* (tr. Scullion, John J.), SPCK, London, 1984.

Whitcomb, John C., Jr., and Morris, Henry M., *The Genesis Flood*, Presbyterian and Reformed, Philadelphia, 1961.

White, A.J. Monty, *What About Origins?*, Duneston Printers, Newton Abbot, 1978.

White, A.J. Monty, *How Old Is the Earth?*, Evangelical Press, Welwyn, 1985.

White, A.J. Monty, *Wonderfully Made*, Evangelical Press, Darlington, 1989.

Whitehouse, Owen C., "Cosmogony", in *A Dictionary of the Bible* (ed. Hastings, James), T. and T. Clark, Edinburgh, 1898–1904 (Vol. 1, pp. 501–507).

Whyte, Lancelot Law, *Internal Factors in Evolution*, Tavistock Publications, London, 1965.

Wilkinson, David A., *In the Beginning God?: Modern Cosmology and Biblical Creation Today: The Origin of the Universe According to Science and the Bible*, The Methodist Church Home Mission Division, London, 1991.

Wilkinson, David, *God, the Big Bang and Stephen Hawking*, Monarch, Tunbridge Wells, 1st edn., 1993; 2nd edn., 1996.

Wiseman, P.J., *Creation Revealed in Six Days*, Marshall, Morgan and Scott, London, 1948.

Wright, John, *Designer Universe: Is Christianity Compatible with Modern Science?*, Monarch, Crowborough, 1994.

Wright, Richard T., *Biology through the Eyes of Faith*, Apollos, Leicester, 1991.

York, Derek, and Farquhar, Ronald M., *The Earth's Age and Geochronology*, Pergamon, Oxford, 1972.

Young, Davis A., *Creation and the Flood*, Baker, Grand Rapids, 1977.
Young, Davis A., *Christianity and the Age of the Earth*, Zondervan, Grand Rapids, 1982.
Young, Davis A., *The Biblical Flood*, Eerdmans, Grand Rapids/Paternoster, Carlisle, 1995.
Young, E.J., *In the Beginning: Genesis Chapters 1 to 3 and the Authority of Scripture*, Banner of Truth, Edinburgh, 1976.
Youngblood, Ronald F. (ed.), *The Genesis Debate*, Nelson, Nashville, 1986; Baker, Grand Rapids, 1990.
Zohar, Danah, *The Quantum Self*, Bloomsbury, London, 1990.
Zohary, Daniel, and Hopf Maria, *Domestication of Plants in the Old World*, Oxford University Press, 2nd edn., 1993.

Supplement

Alexander, Denis R. *Creation or Evolution: Do We Have To Choose?*, Monarch, Oxford and Grand Rapids, 2008.
Atkins, Peter, *On Being: a Scientist's Exploration of the Great Questions of Existence*, Oxford University Press, Oxford, 2011.
Bailey, Lloyd R., *Noah*, University of South Carolina Press, 1989.
Behe, Michael J., *The Edge of Evolution: the Search for the Limits of Darwinism*, Free Press, New York, 2007.
Berry, R.J., "This Cursed Earth: Is 'the Fall' Credible?", *Science and Christian Belief*, Vol. 11, 1999, pp. 29–49.
Berry, R.J., and Jeeves, M., "The Nature of Human Nature", *Science and Christian Belief*, Vol. 20, 2008, pp. 3–47.
Berry, R.J., and Noble, T.A. (eds.), *Darwin, Creation and the Fall*, Apollos, Nottingham, 2009.
Best, Robert M., *Noah's Ark and the Ziusudra Epic*, Enil Press, Fort Myers, Florida, 1999.
Bimson, John J., "Reconsidering a 'Cosmic Fall'", *Science and Christian Belief*, Vol. 18, 2006, pp. 63–81.
Boudreaux, Edward A., and Baxter, Eric C., *God Created the Earth: Genesis of Creation Chemistry*, Central Ohio Creation Research Association, Canal Winchester, Ohio, 2009.
Brown, William P., *The Seven Pillars of Creation: the Bible, Science, and the Ecology of Wonder*, Oxford University Press, 2010.
Byl, John, *God and Cosmos: a Christian View of Time, Space, and the Universe*, Banner of Truth, Edinburgh, 2001.
Carlson, Richard F., and Longman, Tremper, III, *Science, Creation and the Bible: Reconciling Rival Theories of Origins*, IVP Academic, Downers Grove, Illinois, 2010.

BIBLIOGRAPHY

Cela-Conde, Camilo J., and Ayala, Francisco J., *Human Evolution*, Oxford University Press, 2007.

Collins, C. John, "The *wayyiqtol* as 'Pluperfect': When and Why", *Tyndale Bulletin*, Vol. 46, 1995, pp. 117–140.

Collins, C. John, *Genesis 1–4*, P & R Publishing, Phillipsburg, New Jersey, 2006.

Collins, C. John, *Did Adam and Eve Really Exist?: Who They Were and Why It Matters*, Inter-Varsity Press, Nottingham, 2011.

Currid, John D., *A Study Commentary on Genesis*, Vol. 1, *Genesis 1:1–25:18*, Evangelical Press, Darlington, 2003.

Davies, Paul C.W., *The Goldilocks Enigma*, Allen Lane, London, 2006; Penguin, London, 2007/*The Cosmic Jackpot*, Houghton Mifflin Harcourt, Boston, 2007.

Dawkins, Richard, *The God Delusion*, Bantam, London, 2006.

Dembski, William A., *The Design Inference: Eliminating Chance through Small Probabilities*, Cambridge University Press, 1998.

Dembski, William A. (ed.), *Mere Creation: Science, Faith and Intelligent Design*, InterVarsity Press, Downers Grove, Illinois, 1998.

Dembski, William A., *Intelligent Design: The Bridge between Science and Theology*, InterVarsity Press, Downers Grove, Illinois, 1999.

Dembski, William A., *The Design Revolution: Answering the Toughest Questions about Intelligent Design*, InterVarsity Press, Downers Grove, Illinois, 2004.

Dembski, William A., *The End of Christianity: Finding a Good God in an Evil World*, B & H Publishing, Nashville, Tennessee, 2009.

Dembski, William A., and Ruse, Michael (eds.), *Debating Design: from Darwin to DNA*, Cambridge University Press, Cambridge, 2004.

Dembski, William A., and Witt, Jonathon, *Intelligent Design Uncensored*, InterVarsity Press, Downers Grove, Illinois, 2010.

DeYoung, Don, *Thousands not Billions: Challenging an Icon of Evolution, Questioning the Age of the Earth*, Master Books, Green Forest, Arkansas, 2005.

Falk, Darrel R., *Coming to Peace with Science: Bridging the Worlds between Science and Faith*, InterVarsity Press, Downers Grove, Illinois, 2004.

Forrest, Barbara, and Gross, Paul R., *Creationism's Trojan Horse: the Wedge of Intelligent Design*, Oxford University Press, 2004.

Fowler, Thomas B., and Kuebler, Daniel, *The Evolution Controversy: a Survey of Competing Theories*, Baker Academic, Grand Rapids, 2007.

Garner, Paul A., *The New Creationism*, Evangelical Press, Darlington, 2009.

Ganji, M.H., "Post-Glacial Climatic Changes on the Iranian Plateau", in *The Environmental History of the Near and Middle East since the Last Ice Age* (ed. Brice, William C.), Academic Press, London, 1978, Chap. 10.

Gentry, R.V., Glish, G.L., and McBay, E.H., "Differential Helium Retention in Zircons: Implications for Nuclear Waste Containment", *Geophysical Research Letters*, Vol. 9, 1982, pp. 1129–1130.

Hasker, William, *The Emergent Self*, Cornell University Press, Ithaca, 1999.

Haught, John F., *Making Sense of Evolution: Darwin, God, and the Drama of Life*, Westminster John Knox Press, Louisville, 2010.

Hawking, Stephen, and Mlodinow, Leonard, *The Grand Design*, Bantam, London, 2010.

Hawley, John F., and Holcomb, Katherine A., *Foundations of Modern Cosmology*, 2nd edn., Oxford University Press, 2005.

Hill, Carol A., "The Garden of Eden: a Modern Landscape", *Perspectives on Science and Christian Faith*, Vol. 52, 2000, pp. 31–46.

Hill, Carol A., "A Time and a Place for Noah", *Perspectives on Science and Christian Faith*, Vol. 53, 2001, pp. 24–40.

Hill, Carol A., "A Third Alternative to Concordism and Divine Accommodation: the Worldview Approach", *Perspectives on Science and Christian Faith*, Vol. 59, 2007, pp. 129–134.

Hill, Carol A., "Response to P.G. Nelson's 'Numerology in Genesis'", *Perspectives on Science and Christian Faith*, Vol. 60, 2008, p. 144.

Hitchcock, Gavin, "'Good Death': a Common Pattern in the Evolution of Mathematics, Science and Biological Organisms", *Science and Christian Belief*, Vol. 23, 2011, pp. 115–132.

Hughes, Jennifer F., *et al.*, "Chimpanzee and Human Y Chromosomes Are Remarkably Divergent in Structure and Gene Content", *Nature*, Vol. 463, 2010, pp. 536–539.

Humphreys, John, *In God We Doubt: Confessions of a Failed Atheist*, Hodder and Stoughton, London, 2007.

Kulikovsky, Andrew S., *Creation, Fall, Restoration: a Biblical Theology of Creation*, Mentor, Fearn, Ross-shire, 2009.

Lennox, John C., *Seven Days that Divide the World: the Beginning According to Genesis and Science*, Zondervan, Grand Rapids, Michigan, 2011.

Lewin, Roger, *Human Evolution*, 5th edn., Blackwell, Malden, Massachusetts, 2005.

Loechelt, Gary H., "Fenton Hill Revisited: the Retention of Helium in Zircons and the Case for Accelerated Nuclear Decay", www.reasons.org/files/HeliumDiffusionZirconTechnicalPaper.pdf (2008)

Lucas, Ernest C., *Can We Believe Genesis Today?: the Bible and Questions of Science*, 2nd edn., Inter-Varsity Press, Leicester, 2001.

Lucas, Ernest C., "God and 'Natural Evil'", *Faith and Thought*, No. 50, 2011, pp. 16–26.

Maisels, Charles Keith, *The Emergence of Civilization*, Routledge, London and New York, 1990.

McGovern, Patrick E.; Hartung, Ulrich; Badler, Virginia R.; Glusker, Donald L.; and Exner, Lawrence J., "The Beginnings of Winemaking and Viniculture in the Ancient Near East and Egypt", *Expedition*, Vol. 39, No. 1, 1997, pp. 3–21.

BIBLIOGRAPHY

McKee, Jeffrey K., Poirier, Frank E., and McGraw, W. Scott, *Understanding Human Evolution*, 5th edn., Pearson Prentice Hall, Upper Saddle River, New Jersey, 2005.

McWeeny, Roy, "Quantum Chemistry: the First Seventy Years", *Faraday Discussions*, Vol. 135, 2007, pp. 13–30.

Mithen, Steven, *After the Ice: a Global Human History 20,000–5000 BC*, Weidenfeld and Nicolson, London, 2003; Phoenix, London, 2004.

Moore, A.M.T., Hillman, G.C., and Legge, A.J., *Village on the Euphrates: from Foraging to Farming at Abu Hureyra*, Oxford University Press, Oxford, 2000.

Murphy, Nancey, "Nonreductive Physicalism: Philosophical Issues", in *Whatever Happened to the Soul?* (ed. Brown, Warren S.; Murphy, Nancey; and Malony, H. Newton) Fortress Press, Minneapolis, 1998, Chap. 6.

Nelson, P.G., "Free Will in a Deterministic Universe", *Faith and Thought*, No. 44, 2008, pp. 21–26.

Nelson, P.G., "Numerology in Genesis", *Perspectives on Science and Christian Faith*, Vol. 60, 2008, pp. 70–71.

Nelson, P.G., *The Logic of Life: Seeking Truth To Live By*, Avenue Books, Seaford, 2008.

Nelson, P.G., "Another Look at Mature Creation", *Faith and Thought*, No. 49, 2010; www.biblicalstudies.org.uk/pdf/nelson/creation_nelson.pdf

Nelson, P.G., "Another Look at the Genesis Flood", www.biblicalstudies.org.uk/pdf/nelson/flood_nelson.pdf

Nelson, P.G., "Genesis 1–3 as a Theodicy", www.biblicalstudies.org.uk/pdf/nelson/theodicy_nelson.pdf

Nevin, Norman C. (ed.), *Should Christians Embrace Evolution?: Biblical and Scientific Responses*, Inter-Varsity Press, Nottingham, 2009.

O'Connell, Patrick, *Science of To-day and the Problems of Genesis*, Radio Replies Press Society, Minnesota, 1959.

Olson, Walter S., "Has Science Dated the Biblical Flood?", *Zygon*, Vol. 2, 1967, pp. 272–278.

Pennisi, Elizabeth, "ENCODE Project Writes Eulogy for Junk DNA", *Science*, Vol. 337, 2012, pp. 1159–1161.

Phillips, Rod, *A Short History of Wine*, Penguin, London, 2000.

Polkinghorne, John C., *Science and the Trinity: the Christian Encounter with Reality*, Yale University Press, 2004.

Polkinghorne, John C., *Exploring Reality: the Intertwining of Science and Religion*, SPCK, London, 2005.

Polkinghorne, John C., *Reason and Reality: the Relationship between Science and Theology*, SPCK, London, 2011.

Polkinghorne, John C., *Science and Religion in Quest of Truth*, SPCK, London, 2011.

Poythress, Vern S., *Redeeming Science: a God-centred Approach*, Crossway, Wheaton, Illinois, 2006.

Rau, Gerald, *Mapping the Origins Debate: Six Models of the Beginning of Everything*, IVP Academic, Downers Grove, Illinois/IVP, Nottingham, 2012.

Reimer, P.J., *et al.*, "IntCal09 and Marine09 Radiocarbon Age Calibration Curves, 0–50,000 years cal BP", *Radiocarbon*, Vol.51, 2009, 1111–1150

Rose, Jeffrey I., "New Light on Human Prehistory in the Arabo-Persian Gulf Oasis", *Current Anthropology*, Vol. 51, 2010, pp. 849–883.

Ross, Hugh, *A Matter of Days: Resolving a Creation Controversy*, NavPress, Colorado Springs, 2004.

Ross, Hugh, *More than a Theory: Revealing a Testable Model for Creation*, Baker, Grand Rapids, 2009.

Rüst, Peter, "Early Humans, Adam, and Inspiration", *Perspectives on Science and Christian Faith*, Vol. 59, 2007, pp. 182–193.

Ryden, Barbara, *Introduction to Cosmology*, Addison Wesley, San Francisco, 2003.

Seely, Paul H., "Noah's Flood: Its date, Extent, and Divine Accommodation", *Westminster Theological Journal*, Vol. 66, 2004, pp. 291–311.

Shapiro, James A., *Evolution: a View from the 21st Century*, FT Press Science, Upper Saddle River, New Jersey, 2011.

Spieser, E.A., "The Rivers of Paradise", in *Oriental and Biblical Studies* (ed. Finkelstein, J.J., and Greenberg, M.), University of Pennsylvania Press, Philadelphia, 1967, pp. 23–34.

Stiebing, William H., Jr., "A Futile Quest: The Search for Noah's Ark", *The Biblical Archaeology Review*, Vol. 2, No. 2, 1976, pp. 1, 13–20.

Stringer, Chris, and Andrews, Peter, *The Complete World of Human Evolution*, Thames and Hudson, London, 2005.

Teller, J.T., Glennie, K.W., Lancaster, N., and A.K. Singhvi, A.K., "Calcareous Dunes of the United Arab Emirates and Noah's Flood: the Postglacial Reflooding of the Persian (Arabian) Gulf", *Quaternary International*, Vol. 68–71, 2000, pp. 297–308.

Tinker, Melvin, *Reclaiming Genesis: the Theatre of God's Glory – or a Scientific Story?*, Monarch, Oxford, 2010.

Vardiman, Larry, and Humphreys, D. Russell, "A New Creationist Cosmology: in No Time at All", *Acts and Facts*, Vol. 39, No. 11, 2010, pp. 12–15 (Article 5686), Vol. 40, No. 1, 2011, pp. 12–14 (Article 5830), Vol. 40, No. 2, 2011, pp. 12–14 (Article 5870), www.icr.org

Walton, John H., *The Lost World of Genesis One*, InterVarsity Press, Downers Grove, Illinois, 2009.

Young, Davis A., and Stearley, Ralph F., *The Bible, Rocks and Time: Geological Evidence for the Age of the Earth*, IVP Academic, Downers Grove, Illinois, 2008.

Index

INDEX

INDEX